iregamick

First Published in 1982
by Tabb House, 11 Church Street, Padstow, Cornwall.

Reprinted 1985, 1989
First cased edition 1985

Copyright © Keith Chatfield
ISBN 0 907018 17 3 Limp
ISBN 0 907018 44 0 Cased

Illustrations by Joyce Curtis

Printed in Great Britain by The Guernsey Press Co. Ltd, Guernsey, Channel Islands.

## List of Illustrations

## Cornwall 1793

IF THE DUTCH SHIP *Anneke* had been left to the skill of her crew, she might well have been saved from the foaming seas, which dashed her against the rocks at Portheras Cove on that stormy night in May 1793.

Young Dick Tregarrick was one of ninety Cornishmen lined up along the foreshore, who had other plans for the trapped and ailing ship. Together with his father Tom, Ben Trewan, and Maddy Maddocks, Dick found himself party to plundering which was to have the most far-reaching consequences. For the mystery and intrigue that resulted from that night's adventure in the pounding surf were destined to change the course of his whole life.

# Chapter 1

AS THE STORM reached its most vicious peak, lightning struck the engine house at Wheal Mary. The solid, square-foot balk of timber that served as the spring beam snapped like a twig. A split second later, the main shaft of the mine was a plunging nightmare of timber and iron.

At first, the men, toiling and sweating in the depths of the mine, assumed that the muffled roar was an explosion, made by a fellow miner, blasting his way into the tin lode at some distant pitch. But the sudden blanket of suffocating air that rushed in upon them was warning enough of the hell that had struck. It snuffed out their dips, and made their breathing heavy.

They froze like statues, listening.

Damp cold pierced the marrow of their bones.

The deathly silence that followed the explosion was replaced by muttering and unsteady movement, as men fumbled to relight their tallow dips in the entombed blackness. Each sought reassurance that he, for the moment at least, still lived. But to the one person who needed that reassurance of life most of all, none came.

Dick Tregarrick could not move. Paralysed by the rumbling mass that hurtled down the shaft, he was pinned to the granite floor by the thirteen stone dead weight of his father who lay sprawled across him.

Tom Tregarrick's face lay next to his son's.

"You're . . . you're pressin' me chest, Father."

The acrid smell from his father's snuffed dip curled round Dick's nostrils. His father lay very still.

"Father . . . answer me!"

Dick was aware of his father's awful stillness in the pitch black. He listened for his father's breathing, but

3

the sound of water gushing from a nearby level into the shaft drowned all other noise.

"Father?"

There was no response, not the slightest sign of life from the man who, only seconds before, had reached out to grasp the ladder which was to lead them both upwards, to grass and fresh air and home and safety.

The explosion had been sudden; like a cannon being fired into the shaft, with that eerie flash of light, the cry from his father, and then the blackness, the uproar and the ton weight which had struck and now trapped him.

Dick strained every muscle in his twelve-year old body to separate the tangle of his limbs from those of his father.

A clatter of heavy boots on the ladder below jarred sharply above the constant sound of cascading water. A glimmer of light glowed upwards through the shaft. It grew brighter and brighter until a head broke through the gaping hole at the level where he lay.

The head belonged to Ben Trewan, the chief sumpman, whose job it was to make sure that the shafts in the Roscarrock section were sunk to the required level and efficiently maintained.

"Right, boys. Let's 'ave yer! Look alive!" he shouted. "The pumps are knacked! You'll be up to yer neck in water if yer stay there! Don' 'ang about!"

"I can't move!" shouted Dick.

Ben Trewan stepped off the ladder into the level. The ladder continued to shake and clatter with the boots of other men who clambered at full speed to safety.

"Who 'ave we 'ere?"

"Dick Tregarrick! My father's hurt, bad!"

A globule of hot fat fell from Ben's dip onto Dick's cheek as the man knelt over the sprawled bodies.

"I can't move," said Dick.

"No more yer can, like a rabbit in a gin," replied Ben.

4

He grasped Tom's arm and heaved the body clear of the boy.

Dick felt a swirl of water round his head and shoulders. He tried to get up. Ben pressed his ear to Tom Tregarrick's chest.

Dick watched him. "He's . . . he's not dead is he?"

Ben didn't answer.

The shaft was suddenly alive with men. Seven or eight had stepped off the ladder to see what the trouble was. They clustered round Tom's body.

For the moment Dick's legs refused to carry him and he huddled in a crawling position. Water swirled round his hands and knees.

"He is dead, isn't he?" Dick didn't want to hear the answer.

"We'll all be dead if we don't move quickly," said Ben, standing up. "Here," he said to Maddy Maddocks. "You see to the boy's father. I'll get the lad to grass. And you others — keep movin' up."

Someone picked up Dick's helmet and pushed it firmly onto his head.

Dick felt himself being lifted across Ben's broad, damp shoulders.

"Hold on young 'un — you'll be fine."

Water poured down the shaft. The dip on Ben's helmet was immediately doused. The pumps had stopped working the moment the beam snapped, and now rivulets of water emptied into the shaft from every level.

Twelve hundred rungs stretched vertically above Ben Trewan's head. Breathing steadily, he began to edge his way upwards. He called to those above to step aside as he heaved the bewildered boy to the surface.

Muttered questions were directed at him as he passed the men who'd stepped into the nearest level to make way. Ben answered briefly.

Through the sway and jolt of his upward movement, through the rush of water which cascaded over them, Dick formed a vivid picture from the words he picked out of the gloom.

"Accursed storm . . ."

" . . . hit by lightning."

" . . . beam just snapped like a carrot!"

" . . . shaft must've been alive with electricity!"

To Dick Tregarrick the picture was clear. His father had been killed by the lightning that had struck the ladder. He screwed up his eyes tightly and bit so deeply into his bottom lip, it drew blood.

"He is dead isn't he?" The words were pumped out of his jolting body.

"Save yer breath, boy. You'll be all right," said Ben.

Dick was aware of Ben's shoulder digging into the pit of his stomach and he felt sick. He could hear the thunder above the din of rushing water; loud, crashing thunder. A flash of dim light filled the shaft for a split second. Then all was dark again.

At last the nightmare journey ended. Ben Trewan deposited his load feet downwards in the mud at the entrance of the surface level.

In the dim afternoon light obscured by torrential rain, a crowd of a hundred or more jostled, each wanting to help.

"Get you into the dry, boy, and wait. 'Ere!" Ben called to Martha Kerrow. An elderly woman with a hessian apron draped over her head moved forward. "Take the boy into the dry. He's shocked." Ben muttered something else that Dick didn't catch, then turned to go back down the shaft.

Martha put a comforting arm round Dick's shoulders. Dick felt numb.

"My Father's dead!" he whispered. His voice broke as he tried to hold back the tears.

"Now, now, we don't know that," said Martha softly. leading the boy away through the crowd.

"He is. I know he is," said Dick.

He broke from the woman and pushed his way back to the entrance of the shaft. "Father! Father!" He roared the words down into the blackness, sobbing uncontrollably. The rain streamed down his face. "Father! Don't die, Father! Don't die!"

Someone moved towards him, offering a hand to comfort him. Dick spoke softly. "I don't want my father to die. I don't want him to die."

Dick couldn't hold back the sobs, and his young body was convulsed by them. He was aware of countless eyes staring at him; the eyes of strangers. He had to get away from them. The only people he wanted, and he wanted them desperately, were his mother, his brother, his sisters; those who could reassure him of his home and the warmth and security it had always offered.

Through bleared eyes he saw Martha moving towards him. He turned and ran.

He ran with a wild burst of speed. Mud from the slurried pathway bespattered his legs. His boots clawed frantically to gain a foothold.

Torrents of rain pelted his helmet, sluiced his face, and streamed down his chest. Like some mad, drowning animal he hurtled along the track that led from the mine, his arms flailing madly to ward off those who would help him.

He could hear cries of "Stop him!"

"It's Tregarrick's boy!"

"Stop him!"

He instinctively turned left across the moor towards his home, two and a half miles away.

As his boots pounded the track, he gasped for breath; it was the same pathway that he and his father had trod that morning on their way to the mine. He ran like a

7

crazed animal. He ran and ran and ran. At last, his heart and lungs bursting with pain, he stumbled. A fiery golden mass of furze flashed towards him, seeming to beckon him from out of the drab, breathless, sodden, greyness of that wretched day. He crashed through the sharp, tearing foliage and fell. His head crunched on a slab of granite and he lay unconscious.

## Chapter 2

JAGO LUGG had watched Dick's dramatic exit from Wheal Mary with more than casual interest.

Lugg was a sick man. A premature explosion underground had cost him the loss of an eye, and those who knew him reckoned he could count himself lucky not to have lost his head.

The accident had happened five weeks earlier, and for three of those weeks his meagre allowance, from the Doctor and Club Fund, had been augmented by payments due to him from past services with Tom Tregarrick. But for two weeks now he had received nothing. Hence Jago's presence at the mine on this fateful day. He needed money. And he knew there was money in plenty to be had from Tom's most recent exploits at Portheras Cove.

Lugg was a partner in the successful but illegal partnership of Tregarrick, Trewan, Maddocks and Lugg. Part-time smugglers and wreckers, these four men had not missed a single wrecking from Hor Point to Cape Cornwall in fifteen years. Their last expedition had been to Portheras Cove, only three days before.

The Dutch ship, *Anneke*, bound from Nantes to Bristol with a valuable cargo of brandy and saffron, had run aground in a devastating gale-force south westerly. There had been a very good chance of saving her, had she been left to the resources of her crew, but eighty to ninety Cornishmen had other ideas, and the crew were forced to abandon their ship to the wreckers.

The rewards for this enterprise had been excellent, particularly for Tom Tregarrick, Ben Trewan and Maddy Madocks, whose methodical plundering worked well in the general chaos.

Jago Lugg had missed this profitable haul because he was on his sick bed nursing an empty eye socket. His place had been taken by Tom's son, Dick.

Tom had always struggled to prevent his conscience standing between him and the spoils that God saw fit to send his way from time to time. Life as a miner was tough and ill rewarded. So, when providence supplied the opportunities, Tom supplied the human sweat and effort needed to give himself and his family those little extras that an honest life denied them.

Tom, Ben and Maddy earned their legitimate wages underground at Wheal Mary. Maddy had a second string to his bow. He was the local coffin maker. They had worked together on legitimate and illegitimate enterprises long before Jago came onto the scene, and, although they never fully trusted each other, each held a healthy respect for the others' talents. But Tom, Ben and Maddy trusted Jago least of all. And this was due to the strange circumstances in which Jago had been admitted to the partnership.

The three of them had returned one night to a secret hideout to collect half a dozen kegs of brandy which lay concealed there. The brandy was there by the grace of God, and one of the most successful runs from France that Tom had ever organised. Who should they find but Jago Lugg, unconscious, and sprawled at the mouth of the cave, with his leg crushed under a most untimely fall of rock.

Jago, it seemed, had developed a profitable line of business in stealing from those who stole; a career that was to end on the night the rockfall trapped him.

The three men stood and looked at their unwanted guest.

"What shall we do with 'im?" said Ben.

"God in his wisdom had obviously meant to kill the

devil. I reckon we should help 'im finish the job," said Maddy.

"I agree," said Ben.

But Tom didn't.

"Look, Tom, 'e meant to 'elp 'imself to our stuff didn't 'e?' said Maddy. "E's almost dead. We've only got to kill him just a little bit more."

"How do you kill someone just a little bit more? You either kill 'em or you don't!"

"You know what I mean!"

They argued for several minutes but in the end Tom managed to get a more reasonable point of view across to them. So, when Lugg regained consciousness, he was given a choice.

"As far as we're concerned you can go the way your Maker intended — to an early grave," Tom said. Lugg blanched. "Or you can work out your debt to us, for letting you live, by working for me."

Lugg had opted for the chance to live, and when his leg had healed enough for him to be of some use to Tom, Tom used him.

Tom had introduced him to Chegwidden, the Captain at Wheal Mary, who had given the man underground employment where Tom, Ben and Maddy could all keep an eye on him.

The partnership of four had panned out reasonably well for several years. But since Jago lost his eye he'd been out of touch with the others, and now, determined to claim a fair share of the *Anneke*'s plunder, he'd dragged himself from his sick bed to confront his partners, and discover where they had hidden the booty.

He had discovered nothing from Ben and Maddy, who insisted that, since Jago had been unable to take part in the wrecking, he was not entitled to any part of it.

"But we've been mates a long time," pleaded Jago.

"That's as may be," Maddy said, "but we ain't a charity

11

and your place 'as been took by a fresher pair o' eyes and younger legs."

Tom Tregarrick was Jago's last hope. He'd missed Tom on his arrival at Wheal Mary and now, many hours later, he waited in the torrential rain for Tom to surface after his day's work. Smouldering with bitterness, and cursing the fates which had reduced him to this pitiful, outcast wreck of a man, he waited.

When he saw the arrival of Dick Tregarrick on the shoulders of Ben Trewan, he instinctively knew that those 'fresher' eyes and 'younger' legs, referred to by Maddy, belonged to Dick.

Seconds later he heard that Tom was dead.


From Jago's point of view, Tom Tregarrick had chosen a most inconvenient time to die. But then, all at once, Lugg saw in Dick the one link between himself and a much needed share in the spoils of the *Anneke.*

Dick's eyelids strained to lift the heavy weight that seemed to lie upon them. His eyes rolled, vainly trying to focus on the light which penetrated his dark lashes. For several seconds they refused to part.

Dick couldn't remember what had happened to him, and his aching head was even more confused by the strange vision that finally imprinted itself on his brain. Never had he seen that filthy, cobweb-infested roof before.

"A-ha, so you are still in the land o' the livin'!"

Dick turned his head sharply towards the voice. A pain seared through his head, made all the more acute by the prospect of the grimy features of the one-eyed man who smiled at him with a sickly grin.

"I found yer," said Jago, "all torn and shredded in the lea of a furze bush."

Memories flooded back into Dick's mind.

12

"Nasty little argument you had with a slab o' granite." Jago attempted a friendly chuckle. "So I brought you 'ere and patched you up."

As Jago leant forward to bathe Dick's wound, Dick jerked his head away.

"Take it easy boy. I'm not going to 'urt yer."

"I'd rather you left me alone, sir," said Dick.

"Left you alone eh?" smiled Jago. "Well bless my soul, if I'd done that yer'd still be a lyin' with a lump o' granite for a pillow."

Dick felt sick.

"You don' recognise me, do you?" said Jago.

"No, sir, I don't."

"Jago." He paused to let the name sink in. "Jago Lugg . . . remember?"

"I . . . I'm sorry I didn't . . ." Dick stopped.

"You didn't recognise me with one o' me dips snuffed out, did yer?" Jago grinned.

Dick's eyes grew vacant.

"My father's dead." He whispered the words to himself.

"Er . . . yes . . . so I've 'eard say," said Jago, hanging his grizzly head low.

"I must get home," said Dick.

"Me an' yer father were great pals," said Jago. "Yer don' go through adventures like me an' yer father, doing the things we done together, without . . . without gettin' to be very . . ." He broke off. "'Ere! Where you goin'?"

Dick tried to raise himself from the crude wooden bed and felt a sharp tug at his ankles. They were tied by a length of rope to the foot of the bed.

"Just a safety precaution, Dick boy. Yer was thrashing about so wildly, I was afeared yer might throw yersel' to the floor and 'urt yersel'."

Dick bent forward to untie the tight knots which gouged his instep.

There was a knock on the door.

Jago shuffled over to it, lifted the latch, and opened it three or four inches.

"I've brought some food."

It was a girl's voice, gentle and nervous.

"You couldn't've chose a better moment, my little 'andsome," said Jago. "The young 'un's just come round. He must be starvin'."

Jago took the tray of food, making sure the girl did not get the chance to look into the room.

"Is there anything else you need?" asked the voice.

"Not tonight, my little maid. Best get yersel' some sleep."

"But..."

"Get yersel' some sleep I said. You 'eard me."

"Goodnight, Father."

"Goodnight, girl."

Dick's brain pounded. His head felt near to bursting point. He tugged at the unyielding knots round his ankles.

"I want to get home". He blurted out the words.

A firm, rough hand gripped his own. Jago sat on the edge of the bed.

"O' course yer do. O' course yer do."

"I must get home. My mother...my sisters..I must see them." Dick tried to free his hands.

"Now listen. You bin through a sort o' 'ell today, Dick, an' o' course yer must get home. But yer not going to manage without a bit o' rest and a bite to eat. It's three miles o' more to your place."

"Untie me," said Dick.

"All in good time, all in good time ... Now you just..."

Dick twisted his body in one violent movement. His hands snapped free from under Jago's fist. He threw his whole weight at Jago who fell, with a thud, to the floor.

14

Dick landed on top of him, his trapped legs stretched to breaking point by the rope which held them prisoner.

"Why yer li'l'...". Jago, his breath knocked out of him, dragged himself clear of Dick, rolled the boy over onto his face and knelt on his back. Dick gave a yell of pain.

"Right! We'll stop pretendin', eh?"

Jago talked, and Dick listened.

Dick was left in no doubt as to Jago's purpose in bringing him to his home. He wanted to know the whereabouts and the value of the *Anneke*'s haul. It was clear that Maddy and Ben had not talked. And it was clear that Jago's only interest in Dick was to gain this information, which he was determined to do.

"... so I'm askin' yer now. Where did you an' yer father stow the moonshine off the *Anneke*?"

Dick needed time to think. His head throbbed. Jago's knee gouged into the small of his back and the rope burnt into his ankles.

"I...I'll tell you."

Jago took his weight off the boy and Dick eased himself over. His body and mind ached.

"For pity's sake, my father's dead and my mother..." Dick began.

"Listen you," Jago hissed. "My father's dead, my mother's dead, and my wife's dead. Let's talk about the livin' shall we?"

"Why don't you talk to Ben and Maddy? They were your partners. They can take you right to it. I only know roughly where it is."

"Then roughly will have to do for a start," said Jago, "an perhaps if we start off roughly..." He grabbed Dick by the shirt... "yer memory will come back and yer'll be able to tell me exactly where it is."

Dick spoke quietly.

"Lower Gun."

Jago let go of the boy. Lower Gun was a distinct possibility; a disused mine about three miles from Portheras Cove. The boy could be telling the truth.

"Well now," said Jago, "that's not bad for a rough memory is it? It's a start ain't it? On'y trouble is Lower Gun's a big place, an' I on'y got one eye. So I need a bit more o' yer memory to 'elp me, don't I?"

Dick said nothing.

Jago grabbed Dick by the shirt again. "Don' I?"

Dick paused. "The main shaft. Seven deep and always right," he said softly.

A leer spread slowly across Jago's face. Tom Tregarrick always used a simple code like that to lead him back to a hideout.

"'Alf chance, Dick Tregarrick, you might just be tellin' me the truth, little man," said Jago. "An' what shall I find seven deep and always right?"

"Kegs of brandy, bags of saffron, and some chests."

"What was in the chests?"

"I don't know. Honest."

"You've bin more than 'elpful," smiled Jago, letting go of Dick's shirt.

He put his hand under his top coat and drew a knife from his belt.

"Course boy, if you bin lyin' ter me..."he said, "I'll catch you an' I'll bind you up in a net an' stake you out at low water."

Dick didn't move.

"Then the sharks an' crabs'll get you, boy. Remember that."

Jago paused. Then he slid the knife spitefully between the raw bruised flesh of Dick's ankles and the rope that held him. Dick winced, and a second later clenched his teeth in pain as the man viciously pulled the knife through the rope. Dick was free.

Jago walked slowly over to the door and lifted the latch.

Dick stood up, slowly.

"I'm not sure where I am," he said.

"Follow the pathway to the larger track. Turn right. In 'alf a mile or so yer'll see Wheal Mary. I think yer know yer way from there."

Dick moved towards the door. As he neared it, Jago closed it.

"There's no need to tell Maddy or Ben about our little chat. An' remember...if you bin lyin' ter me, I know where ter find yer. And believe me...I shall."

Lugg opened the door. Dick walked into the next room and straight through it towards the door directly in front of him. His miner's helmet lay on a small table by the door. He picked it up, lifted the latch, swung open the door and stepped quickly outside, pulling the door closed behind him.

A stench that rose from slimy mounds of decaying refuse that lay at his feet made him retch. Jago Lugg was not in the habit of burying or burning his garbage.

The preacher had always insisted that 'Cleanliness be next to godliness.' For once Dick thought he understood. This was an ungodly place, and Jago Lugg was an ungodly man. Dick shuddered.

It was almost dark. The rain had stopped and the dark grey clouds were rolling away to show a deep, darkening blue of evening. Dick had a three mile walk in front of him.

## Chapter 3

CAPTAIN CHEGWIDDEN heaved himself into the saddle and trotted down the rutted pathway from Wheal Mary towards the moorland track. His mine was rapidly filling with water, and his first priority had been to get the splintered beam in the engine house repaired and the pumps working again.

He had set the wheels in motion for repairing the damage and now, tired as he was, his problem was to see Tregarrick's widow and assure her...

"Heh!" he grunted. "Assure her of what?" He stirred his horse into a canter. The only thing he could assure her of was that her husband was dead, and that the funeral expenses would be met from the available fund.

Shrewd and capable in mining affairs, Chegwidden cared for the men who worked in his mine. It made his present task more difficult.

He reined-in as he approached the track and steered his mount left towards the Tregarrick homestead.

Tom Tregarrick, like so many miners, had built his own cottage. He had cleared the waste croft land by blasting the rocks, carving for himself a tiny plateau on which to build a simple two-room cottage with a thatched roof. The lower room was rectangular with a lime-ash floor. The upper room had a slanting high-pitched roof. The walls were built of cob, a mixture of clay stiffened with chopped straw, beaten hard like concrete, and plastered.

Chegwidden tied his horse to the neat white fencing which bounded the front garden plot. The door was opened by Martha Kerrow.

"Oh Cap'n sir, it's kind of you to come."

Chegwidden entered the room, which served as kitchen

19

and living room for the whole family and bedroom for Ruth and Tom.

Ruth lay white and still on the bed, partly concealed by curtains. Chegwidden walked over to the bedside.

"Mrs Tregarrick." He paused. He'd done this many times, but each one was a different and disagreeable experience. "It's little comfort, Mrs Tregarrick, but you are not alone. There are many who share your sorrow and feel privileged to have known Tom."

The woman made no reply.

Chegwidden spoke slowly and deliberately. "The practical comfort I can offer is to assure you that all urgent matters will be taken care of and supervised by me, personally. I shall do all in my power to ensure that you and your children are carried beyond this tragic day with food and care and friends. I hope I may count myself a friend."

Ruth moved. Her face turned slowly towards Chegwidden; a pretty, young face. Tears slowly welled in her deep blue eyes. She blinked them away.

"Thank you," she said quietly. Tears now streamed down the narrow lines of dampness across her cheeks.

"She's desperate to see her son, Dick," whispered Martha. "He ran away from the mine and hasn't come home yet. Mr Trewan and my husband have been out scouring the moors for three hours but there's still no sign of him."

"I'll make sure that every available man joins in the search."

"It's good of you to call."

"Goodbye, Mrs Tregarrick. I shall be at hand for any help you may need."

Ruth nodded.

"Will you stay for a brandy?" asked Mrs Kerrow.

"No, but thank you for the offer. I cannot rest until I know that Dick is safe. The boy will be more comfort to his mother than any of us."

Mrs Kerrow opened the door and Chegwidden left.


Dick passed the entrance to Wheal Mary. A sharp pain in his side forced him to stop for a moment. In the silence Dick was aware of the soft crunch of footsteps on the track behind him. They continued for several steps before they, too, stopped. The pain in his side eased and he walked on, straining his ears to detect the sound of footsteps other than his own. He stopped. The footsteps behind him stopped. He started. They started.

He regained his breath and ran. Rounding a bend, he leapt off the track and crouched low behind a block of granite. He held his breath, waiting for his pursuer to catch up with him.

The footsteps, treading softly, drew nearer.

A dim shadow, cloaked from head to foot, glided past. It paused as it rounded the bend to listen for the footsteps ahead. On hearing nothing, the shadow hurried forward at a faster pace.

Dick slid out from his hiding place. The cloaked shadow moved quickly ahead of him. Dick judged that the person was about the same height as himself, but trod with an amazingly light step.

Dick had moved to within twenty yards of the shadowy figure when it stopped. Dick burst into a run. He hurled himself towards the figure, who turned in alarm as Dick lunged and grabbed at the cloak. Whoever it was let out a startled, high pitched cry and ran, leaving the cloak in Dick's fists.

Dick dropped the cloak and bounded after his quarry. Grabbing it by the arm, he spun the person round to face him. The wide eyed features of a pale young girl stared into his face. Lank, matted ringlets stuck untidily to the perspiration on her brow.

"Who are you? Why are you following me?" said Dick sharply.

"Lizzy." The breathless voice was soft and nervous.

"Who?"

"Lizzy . . . Lizzy Lugg, Jago's daughter."

Dick recognised the voice. It belonged to the girl who had brought food to the door when he lay bound to Jago's bed.

"What do you want?"

"I . . . I want to help."

"Your father sent you after me, didn't he? Didn't he?" Dick grabbed the girl's arm roughly.

"My father is a sick man. I followed you to warn you . . ."

For several minutes they stood, facing each other in the dim glow of moonlight.

Dick let go of the girl's arm.

"Well, go on," said Dick, "Warn me."

"My father wants his share of the spoils that you and your father stole from the *Anneke* . . ."

"Stole!" Dick spoke sharply.

"What else do you call taking what doesn't belong to you?"

"The *Anneke* was there for the taking. If it hadn't been us, it would have been others."

"Just because others thieve and kill..."

"Kill! Who said anything about killing? I haven't time to listen to snivelling preachings from the likes of you."

Dick pushed her aside and set off at a cracking pace for home. The girl's comments disturbed him. Of course wrecking and smuggling were against the law. But everybody did it. Lizzy made it sound as if he and his father were no better than common criminals.

"Listen!" called the girl urgently, trying to keep pace with him.

"I'm listening," said Dick, without slowing.

22

"My father intends to take all the pickings from the *Anneke* for himself."

"And you've got the cheek to accuse my father and me of stealing?" shouted Dick angrily.

"Nothing will stop him..."

"We'll see about that."

"He's a sick man. He's killed men before and he'll kill again."

"I know. D'you think my father hasn't told me about Jago Lugg?" Dick spat the name from his mouth.

"My father's already left for Lower Gun."

Dick stopped. The thought of Lugg checking his story so quickly sent a shiver of fear through him.

Lizzy pulled up, trying to catch her breath.

"What can he hope to find tonight?"

"No sooner had you left than he grabbed helmet, dips and rope and was gone. He said that Ben and Maddy had no right to cut him out and he'd get even with them."

Dick set off again.

"He means to find out if you were telling the truth," said Lizzy, running once more to keep up with him. "Were you telling the truth?"

Dick didn't answer.

"Curse you, Dick Tregarrick! If that treasure ain't there, you'll die on the next spring tide. Don' you understand me?"

Before Dick could speak, the sound of hooves, cantering towards them, made him stop.

He grabbed the girl and pulled her off the track. They crouched behind a furze bush as horse and rider sped past. Barely had they rounded the bend when the steady rhythmic beat of hooves became a discordant clatter and the horse gave an ear piercing whinny.

Muffled shouts and the clink of bridle echoed in the still night air as the rider grappled to control his startled beast.

"They've found your cloak," whispered Dick. "It must've looked like a body lying there."

There was a long pause. Then the rider set off again.

"Who was it?" whispered Lizzy.

"Chegwidden," said Dick. "He's the mine cap'n. He must have been to see my mother."

"Why?" asked Lizzy.

"To tell her that my father was killed today."

Lizzy stared at him. "I'm sorry, I didn't know."

"Well, now you do," said Dick rising and setting off at a run towards his home. "Now you do," he shouted back at the girl. "And he was a good father. And I wish it had been yours who'd died instead!"

Lizzy watched him go.

## Chapter 4

THE SILHOUETTE of the derelict engine house stood out black against the midnight blue of the sky. Lower Gun was a sinister place, and tonight, as Jago limped towards it, it looked like the devil's own landmark.

His eye pained him; not the one he could see out of, but the one he didn't have any more. The pain aggravated his bitterness and swelled his determination to get the better of those who had chosen to discard him.

He had worked with Tom Tregarrick for six years and knew how Tom's mind worked. If the treasures from the *Anneke* lay beneath his feet, and Dick had told him the right code, Jago could go straight to them. If Dick had not told him the truth, he would know. Whichever way his luck went that night, Jago Lugg would either be a wealthier man, or he would have to teach Dick Tregarrick a lesson he would never forget.

Jago stumbled round the dilapidated clusters of outer buildings. He made for the entrance to the main shaft, which was let into the side of a steep hillock, some twelve feet high.

It was boarded up. He lit one of his dips, and shielding the flame against the night wind, held it towards the entrance. In a matter of seconds the fresh breeze extinguished the light. But in those precious seconds Jago had seen two things which pleased him. The timbers had recently been tampered with, and the marks showed clearly which boards could be prised open easily. He took the mattock from his belt and set to work.

Once inside, he lit a dip and pushed it into the large ball of clay which fixed it to his helmet.

He estimated it must be getting on for ten o'clock. By the time Dick Tregarrick, Ben Trewan and Maddy

Maddocks compared notes, sometime next morning at the earliest, Jago Lugg would have struck.

Cursing the pain which still nagged in his eye socket, he set off into the eerie darkness that closed in behind him.

He knew that Tom Tregarrick worked his codes in fathoms, and this knowledge gave him confidence as he began his descent of the main shaft. The ladder, with the exception of the odd rung, was in good condition.

"Seven deep, always right," he muttered to himself. "So, we're talking of seven fathoms deep and keeping to the right."

Suddenly his right foot plunged into ice cold wetness. Jago withdrew it quickly and looked down. The ladder on which he perched continued downwards into a thousand feet of inky black water. Jago shuddered, and cursed his bad fortune.

On looking round, however, he realised that he had arrived at the entrance to an underground level. He decided it must be the seven fathom level, his first objective. He noted that the water came a third of the way up the tunnel wall.

"Trust Tregarrick to choose a level 'alf flooded," he muttered to himself.

He stepped gingerly from the ladder, his foot groping for the submerged floor of the tunnel. The water lapped his thighs. It was bitterly cold, but he waded on.

Somewhere along this god-forsaken, black, half-submerged tunnel, there was enough moonshine to keep Jago Lugg happy for many a month, perhaps many a year. The thought of it urged him on.

In the murk ahead he could see the main tunnel sweeping round to the left, while another forked off to the right. Jago turned right.

"Curse you, Tom Tregarrick!" Jago spat the words

from his mouth, as he felt the water rising above his waist. The tunnel sloped downwards.

He paused. Strange sounds echoed faintly from somewhere further along the tunnel; hollow, dull thuds.

"Well, they 'ain't the piskies I'm sure on that," he muttered to himself. Jago was not a superstitious man and dismissed as utter nonsense the tales he'd heard of the wee folk who were supposed to live underground.

He moved on. The hollow thudding grew louder, turning to a gentle booming, as Jago dragged each leg, made heavy by his sodden clinging trousers, towards the noise.

He stopped. Suddenly he knew what it was. It was the sound of wooden kegs, gently nudging against each other; gently moved by the eddying waters in which they lay.

"Kegs of brandy!" Jago whispered the words through clenched teeth. "Oh, you good boy, Dick Tregarrick!" He started to move forward again, summoning every ounce of speed from his sagging legs. "Oh, you good boy! So you did tell Jago the truth!"

The dull, hollow boom gave way to Jago's yelps and hoots, as he surged through the water, causing a wash behind him. He could see a bend in the tunnel ahead of him. One, two, three, four, five more steps...

He stopped. The fluttering light of his dip picked out the scene for him in shades of dull yellow. His final hoot of triumph was cut short. His mouth stayed open. His eye bulged. A sharp pain cut through his heart.

Floating on the water, nudging the granite walls of the cavern in which he found himself, was the unmistakable shape of a coffin.

Although Jago had stopped, the wave, caused by the previous surge of his body, carried on. It lapped the sides of the wooden box, and as if to herald his arrival, the

27

sonorous boom of coffin against granite echoed loudly round the cavern.

Jago didn't move. The shock of coming upon such a grim reminder of death had all but stopped his heart. Now it pounded against his rib cage.

He could not turn and leave. He would have to investigate this cavern which lay so conveniently seven fathoms deep. This had to be it. The treasure must lie at this very place under the black water that lapped about him . . . and the coffin.

Jago was no stranger to killing, yet the thought of sharing this silent chamber with a corpse, sent a chill down his spine.

Slowly and deliberately, he moved towards the coffin. He touched it.

"S'only a bit o' wood en it? Shaped in a special way."

He pushed it firmly up against the granite wall, and taking the mattock from his belt, he wedged the pointed end under the lid. He began to prise the lid upwards. But before he had raised one portion half an inch, the nails on either side of his lever refused to give any more.

Whoever nailed down this coffin had not meant it to be opened.

Jago moved his mattock to the next nail, and the next, until the whole of one side was loosened. When the end nails had been freed in the same way, he stuffed the mattock back into his belt. Then, with the coffin wedged against the wall, he prepared himself for a powerful, upward heave of the lid to force the far side row of nails out of their sockets.

Amidst a cacophany of splashes, splintering, creaks and grinding metal, the lid shot upwards.

It is difficult to understand why the sight of the corpse shocked him. After all, it was a coffin. But, during his toil, Jago had convinced himself that some sort of booty had been stored in this strange casket. It was certainly a handy container by which the wreckers might transport their ill-gotten gains.

Once away from the immediate area of the wreck, people might think twice before inspecting too closely the contents of a coffin. The prospect of a solemn group of wreckers, tidily carrying away their plunder with such dignity, had brought a grin to his face.

"Trust ol' Tom Tregarrick to think o' that one."

Jago had been quite unprepared for the body which lay there.

Again he felt that stabbing pain through his heart. His body shivered, not from the icy water in which he stood up to his waist, but from the shock of being confronted by such a spectre, in this sepulchral vault. Death was with him.

It was the body of a seafaring man, and, judging from his clothing and the insignia on his cap, he had been a mariner of some rank.

"A cap'n," muttered Jago through his teeth, "e's nothing short of a captain."

He peered at the corpse in the eerie glow of his candle.

Just as the rank of the man was easy to establish, so was the cause of his death. A dull, heavy object had clearly crashed into the man's skull.

Jago had seen such ugly sights before. He knew, only too well, the damage that a weighty chunk of granite could inflict on a human skull.

The initial shock over, Jago began a systematic search of the man's pockets. He could scarcely believe his luck. The man's killer had not ransacked the body.

"Couldna' bin a seasoned wrecker," thought Jago, as he pocketed a few Dutch coins, a fob watch, two gold rings and some personal documents.

"Strange that," he thought, as he struggled to get the man's boots off. They were in excellent condition. He couldn't imagine Ben or Maddy not ransacking the body if they'd done the killing. He'd seen how those two worked.

"They'd've 'ad the clothes off 'is back before the body touched the ground," he muttered.

Jago yanked the second boot off.

"I bet it's somethin' to do with young Dick..."

The thought made him pause. "...Well I never...I wonder if young Dick's done 'is first killin'?"

There was something distinctly odd about this sea captain, lying seven fathoms under the ground, floating gently in his well-constructed, watertight coffin.

Jago's finger now examined the lining of the man's cap, the sort of place a person would put something if it was very important. Indeed the document, which Jago now eagerly extracted, was important. He unfolded it.

It was dated 4th February, 1793, and addressed to Captain Ploos Von Amstel, Master of the *Anneke*. It read: 'Upon presentation of this document to Lord Sebastian Kegwallader of Park Street, Bristol, together with the four chests which I, the undersigned, hereby place in your care; and upon the provision that the chests are fully bound, with seals intact, you shall receive the sum of 100 (one hundred) guineas.
I wish it known to no man of your mission.
Signed
Henri, Comte-de-Valois'

At the foot of the letter were some scribbled figures, not in the same handwriting nor, indeed, the same ink as the main letter. They read as follows:
'4 chests of 50 pounds = 200 pounds
1 gold coin — 125 grains — say 40 or 50 to the pound
Say 10,000 coins'

There was a ring round the 10,000.

Jago read the document again.

So the haul from the *Anneke* had been a good one, an exceptionally good one! The brandy and saffron were only a part of it. "There seems to be a small question of some ten thousand gold coins as well — judgin' by the reckonin' o' some interested party."

Jago looked at the captain. "I wonder if that could 'a' bin you?"

He carefully placed the document in a top pocket of his outer coat. Then systematically he set about treading the invisible floor of the cavern for the treasure that he felt sure must be there. It took him a long time.

An hour later he'd trodden every square inch twice over. The four chests of gold coins were not there. Neither was there any sign of brandy or saffron.

Dick Tregarrick had lied to him. Never had he felt such bitterness. The most valuable haul that Tom had made, and he, Jago Lugg, had been cut out! But he smiled at the thought that Tom Tregarrick would not now benefit from his last wrecking. "An' I promise yer one thing Tom, my old friend, that's if yer ghost's got ears to 'ear me! Yer son Dick won't live to benefit from yer last efforts neither. Jago Lugg'll see to that!"

He moved slowly towards the coffin.

"Well, my ol' shipmate . . . I don' suppose you'll mind drownin'. After all's a little more dignified than just a rottin' there."

Jago grasped the edge of the coffin to push it under the water.

"Beats me why they didn't leave you on the beach a long o' the rest of 'em." Jago paused. "Why should someone 'ave gone to so much trouble over just another dead body? Heh? Poor ol' devil. You'll not be fussing over yer hundred guineas will yer? Nor yer ten thousand gold coins..."

Jago stopped himself just in time from submerging the floating captain.

31

"Why o' course! What's one hundred guineas alongside ten thousand? It must 'a' crossed the cap'n's mind to pinch the stuff. He must've wrote the scribblin'! An' with 'is body out o' the way, people are gonna think 'e pinched it and's still alive to enjoy it! O' course! Why you cunnin' ol' devil Tom, you cunnin' ol' devil!"

It was suddenly very clear to Jago that the captain's corpse could be of tremendous value to him. With the captain's body as proof, he could save the military the trouble of looking for a sea-captain on the run. He might even persuade them to put a noose round Dick Tregarrick's neck; not to mention Ben's and Maddy's.

"Maddy Maddocks; coffin maker!"

The jig-saw was falling into place.

"They're all in it! I got the proof!

With his head bursting with schemes, Jago fitted the lid back onto the coffin and roughly hammered it down. Then he began to push the coffin back towards the shaft.

He steered his grisly cargo to the ladder, uncoiled the rope from his shoulder and made ready to haul his priceless discovery to the surface.

Leaving the coffin to float by the entrance to the seven fathom level, he took the loose end of the rope and dragged his weary body up the ladder to the level above. He then looped the end of it over one of the stanchions which held the ladder in place and began hauling the coffin upwards.

After several minutes of extreme effort, he eased the casket into the entrance of the level for a moment's respite.

Nearing exhaustion, but determined to complete the task he'd begun, he prepared himself for the final haul.

Grasping the end of the rope, he dragged himself up the remaining rungs. Soon, his precious load was resting in the opening to the first level.

Only a few feet to go now to the surface.

At the top, he found a good foothold and began to pull. He kept his eye on the edge of the shaft at the top of the ladder. Any second now he would see the coffin, rising from the depths. It would then be easy to hide it in one of the disused buildings at Lower Gun, while he worked on the next stage of his scheme.

One end of the coffin edged up above the top of the ladder. Jago paused. Then, summoning every last ounce of strength, he heaved. There was an ominous grating noise and the coffin, already tilting at an alarming angle, gently slid out of its rope cradle.

Jago fell backwards as the weight on the end of the rope no longer balanced his straining effort. He fell, hard, against the granite floor, and the coffin, with its invaluable dead contents, plummeted down the shaft.

Jago heard the echoing crashes as it fell, rebounding and splintering against the granite-walled shaft. The noise of breaking wood told him that the coffin would no longer float. Then a resounding splash told him that his precious evidence had hit the water and within seconds it would be covered by a thousand feet of water.

Jago lay where he had fallen. For a moment he could not move.

## Chapter 5

IT WAS MIDNIGHT. The news of Dick's safe return had been passed to those out searching for the boy, and all had gone home except Ben Trewan and Maddy Maddocks. They now sat round the hearth in the Tregarrick Cottage with Mrs Kerrow, Ruth Tregarrick, and Dick.

Ruth bathed her son's bruised ankles in cool water.

"Wait 'til I get my hands on Jago," said Ben. "He'll wish 'e'd never been born."

"At least he won't find anything at Lower Gun," said Maddy, and then added under his breath, "I hope."

"But what's going to happen? Jago knows by now Dick was lying," said Ruth. "He's an evil man."

"If he's been snooping around Lower Gun, he won't come this way tonight. There'll be no work at the mine tomorrow. It'll take a few days to sort those pumps out," said Maddy. "Ben and me'll pay Master Lugg a visit, nice an' early, before he thinks of setting out to find Dick."

"So we shall. But first things first," said Ben. "Tom's death has left a load of problems, and not least for dear Ruth. We want you to know, Ruth, that you and yer family will not want for friends nor money while there's still breath left in the likes o' Maddy and me. That's so, isn't it, Maddy?"

Maddy nodded.

"Friends maybe," said Mrs Kerrow, "but money? Why you two never have a couple of halfpennies to rub together."

"Aha," said Ben. "That was before the *Anneke* chose to run aground...eh, Maddy?"

"A few kegs of brandy and bags of saffron don't exactly add up to a fortune," said Martha.

"No, you're right. But that wasn't all there was, was it?" Ben addressed the question to Dick and winked at him.

"Now look here Ben Trewan, what you holdin' back from us?" said Martha.

No one spoke.

"What you hidin' Ben?" said Ruth, softly.

"To tell you the truth, Maddy and me aren't hiding anything. It's young Dick here. He knows a thing or two that even we don't know. Yer see ... how can I put it...?"

"There was some other stuff but Ben and me never rightly got the chance to see it too closely," said Maddy.

"What are you two on about?" said Mrs Kerrow. "You were both there, weren't you?"

"Well, yes and no," said Ben. "You see..." He paused. "Something cropped up, and Tom sent me and Maddy on a special sort of errand. It was Tom and young Dick 'ere who 'id the stuff."

"What with one thing and another, we haven't got round to Dick telling us exactly what it was, or where it's hid, have we my boy?" said Maddy, pointedly.

The atmosphere had suddenly grown brittle. Martha felt it at once.

"What was so special about this errand which took you away?"

"Well, that we're not free to say," said Ben, "but havin' done as we was told, we was a bit put out when, for no reason as we could see, Tom went very secretive on us."

"You mean he didn't tell you what the stuff was nor where 'e put it?" asked Martha.

"That's about the size of it," said Maddy.

"I'm sure he meant to," said Ben, quickly.

"O' course he meant to, and that's quite enough of this talk," said Martha. "O' course Tom would have told

you all in good time, had the poor man been spared.
You've been working together long enough to know
that."

Ben and Maddy looked at each other. Now was not the
time to talk about Tom.

"You're right," said Ben. "And we'll not be worrying
Dick tonight of all nights." He put his arm around the
boy's shoulders. "All in good time, eh my boy? In the
meantime, we'll keep Jago off your back, Dick. That's a
promise. Then, when the time is right, we'll have a little
chat about — the stuff and what's best to be done with
it. . .eh boy?"

Dick nodded, but said nothing.

"We'll keep our little secret in return for you sharing
yours, eh?" said Maddy.

Ben shot him an ugly look.

"Look Ruth," said Martha, "are you going to be all
right if we go now? I think we should let you get some
sleep."

"Yes, I need some sleep, and to be alone with Dick,"
said Ruth.

"Come along," said Martha to Ben and Maddy. "I
want a word with you two."

They took their leave.

Ruth climbed the wooden ladder to the upper room to
make sure that her three younger children were sleeping
soundly. As yet, they did not know of their father's
death. Her younger son, John, would never remember
him.

She descended the ladder slowly.

Dick gazed into the lamp on the table. He was aware
of his mother's presence.

"It's been a dreadful day, Dick." His mother spoke
softly. She sat down in the chair by the hearth.

"Father inspected the lode of copper in the Goldsworthy

36

today. It's rich. He said he'd make a bid for the pitch. He wanted me to work it with him."

Ruth did not speak.

"It's Setting Day tomorrow. I shall bid for the Goldsworthy. I shall work it on my own."

"You're too young."

"I'm old enough."

"We'll talk about it with Cap'n Chegwidden."

"Father told me from the day the *Anneke* went aground — I'd proved myself a man." He paused. "Something terrible happened that day."

"Tell me." Ruth waited.

"I can't tell you. I can't tell anyone," said Dick. "Father told me not to tell anyone."

Ruth looked at her son.

"What else was there besides brandy and saffron?" she asked.

Dick stared into the lamp again.

"You can't take it all on your young shoulders."

Dick buried his face in his hands.

## Chapter 6

THE BATTERING ON THE DOOR was enough to waken the dead, but not Jago Lugg. He had returned home in the early hours, dropped on his bed, fully clothed, and fallen into a deep sleep.

Lizzy opened the door to Ben and Maddy.

"We've come to see how yer father's feelin' this mornin'," said Ben.

"He's still asleep."

"I bet he is," said Maddy. "He ought to get to bed earlier. A man in his condition needs all the rest he can get."

Ben pushed his way past the girl. Maddy followed him into the cottage.

"Don't wake him. He's a very sick man," said Lizzy.

"Then 'e should keep to his bed instead o' puttin' the fear o' God into boys," said Maddy, walking towards the only other door leading from the room.

Lizzy quickly placed herself between it and Maddy.

"I'll see if he's awake," she said.

"An' if 'e's not, wake 'im, an' tell 'im that two of his mates would like a very urgent word with 'im," said Ben.

The girl opened the door and disappeared through it. She stood looking at the sleeping figure of her father.

"A pity to wake him, isn't it?"

Lizzy jumped, startled by Maddy, who had followed her in.

"Don't be frightened," said Ben, standing in the doorway. "We're not going to 'urt 'im."

The girl stood her ground.

"It's between him an' us, so you get his breakfast on the go. He'll be ready to eat you out o' house an' 'ome time we finished with 'im," said Maddy.

"Come on, there's a good maid," said Ben.

Jago stirred. The girl looked anxiously from Ben to her father back to Ben again. Then she quietly left the room, leaving the door ajar. Maddy closed it.

Ben gave Jago a nudge. Jago grunted. Maddy's nudge was not so gentle. Jago snorted and opened his eye. It took a second or two for his tired brain to realise that he had company. He lay still.

"Well... well... what the 'ell do you two want?"

"We've come with a message," said Ben. Maddy bent low and stared straight into Jago's face. "An' it's such a simple one that even you are goin' to understand it," he said.

Jago said nothing.

"Do you feel in an understandin' frame of mind?" said Maddy. "'Cos if you don't, we shall 'ave to help you a bit."

"Very brave," said Jago. "Two fit men onto one invalid."

"It's about as good as one man, invalid or not, onto one boy," said Ben.

"You don't wan' to believe everythin' you 'ear."

"What are these ropes for?" asked Ben, picking up the freshly cut ends of the ropes that had bound Dick's ankles. You usually strap yerself into bed, do you? Afraid o' fallin' out?"

"I don' 'ave to explain things in my own 'ome to the likes of you."

"No," said Ben, "an' we 'aven't come to ask for explanations."

"Just brought a message," said Maddy.

"If you lay another finger on Dick Tregarrick, or pester 'im in any way, it'll not only be the worse for you," said Ben, "it'll be the end of you. Understand?"

"I've a nice spare coffin," said Maddy.

39

Jago heaved himself up onto an elbow. "Oh yes!" he said, "you're good at makin' coffins." He paused. "Bit too good, I'd say."

Ben and Maddy stared at him. Jago was encouraged by their silence. "You'll 'ave to learn, Maddy. If you want a coffin to sink, you 'ave to leave a few 'oles in it. You didn't know you made coffins so well that they floated, did yer?" he chuckled. "You are indeed a very good coffin maker."

Ben and Maddy said nothing. Their silence told Jago that his guesswork must be accurate.

"Last night," Jago went on, "I managed to salvage a very fine example of your coffin making." He smiled. "It was too good to be left at the bottom of Lower Gun." He paused again. "So I've put it somewhere nice an' safe. I thought there might be others who could be interested in your workmanship. Could bring you a lot o' new business. Might even give you the chance to make your own coffin."

"You've just brought your own headstone a few years earlier," said Maddy, threateningly. He moved towards him.

"'Old it," said Ben. Maddy stopped. "He's bluffin'."

Ben cursed inwardly. Tom's plan had, indeed, been to throw suspicion on the missing captain, and give himself the breathing space he needed to dispose of the gold; the gold that Ben and Maddy had never seen. Jago's discovery altered things, for they hadn't bargained on *him* discovering the corpse.

"You could be right," said Jago. "I could be bluffin'. But yer don't know do yer? At this moment you're wonderin' 'ow I knew there was a coffin in Lower Gun You're wonderin' if I know what's in it. Well, when you've had time to sort it all out, you'll realise that Jago Lugg's in a very powerful position to bargain with you. You could be sorry you tried to cut me out."

40

The situation had taken an unexpected turn. If Jago did have the coffin, it could easily be traced back to Maddy. And if the authorities got as far as Maddy, they would soon get to Ben and Dick.

Ben had nothing to bargain with. He didn't know where the stuff was, nor its value. He decided to get back to the original plan that he and Maddy had come with.

"We came with a simple message, Jago," said Ben. "Lay off the boy, or we'll lower you down Rocky Cove an' let go the rope."

"Don' you threaten me. You may've come with a simple message but you'll be goin' away with a few problems you 'adn't bargained for, won't you?" leered Jago.

"Just lay off the boy," said Ben.

"I've worked 'ard alon'side o' you two and Tom, an' I earnt every penny due to me," said Jago. "Now the first wreckin' I miss . . . an' it's the biggest, ain't it?"

There was no answer.

"Well, you needn't answer, 'cos I 'appen to know it was the biggest. An' all o' a sudden you wan' to keep it all to yerselves." Jago was enjoying the situation. "Well, Jago Lugg's got other ideas. You share the spoils of the *Anneke* with me, an' I'll give you a second chance to get rid of yer coffin . . . an' it's contents."

"We're not interested in your coffin," said Maddy.

"Let's go," said Ben. "We've said what we came to say."

Lizzy, who was preparing something to eat, glanced up as the two men left.

"We've got trouble," said Ben, as soon as they were out of earshot of Jago's cottage.

"Who's goin' to believe a man like Jago, even supposin' he has got the coffin?"

"Don't be a fool. If he's got the coffin, and its contents, 'is story's not goin' to take much believin'. Anyway, that

41

wasn't all I was thinking of," said Ben. "We need Dick to tell us where the stuff is."

Deep in thought, the two men made their way towards Wheal Mary.

## Chapter 7

DICK WOKE UP to the clatter made by his sister Meg, aged ten. She was preparing breakfast. His mother's bedroom was still curtained off.

"Ssh, you'll wake Mother," he warned.

"Sorry," whispered Meg, "but it's difficult to get breakfast with sleeping bodies all round you without waking some of them."

A loud cry from the baby upstairs told the household that he had done with sleep, and a few seconds later the sound of a rattle and singing noises from sister Beckie, who was six, indicated that she was awake and trying to calm her baby brother.

"You look dreadful," said Meg. "Why weren't you in bed?"

Before Dick could answer, his mother pulled the curtain aside and stepped out of her bedroom.

Meg stared at her white face.

"Are you all right, Mother?"

"A little tired. We had friends last night and they stayed late."

"And one of them was Uncle Ben, wasn't it?" said Meg. "I can still smell his tobacco."

She opened the door to let in some fresh air.

The morning was bright and warm. The previous day's thunderstorm had cleared the way for summery weather. It was May, and the scents of the wild grasses and flowers had an immediate, sweetening effect on the air inside the cottage.

Breakfast was a simple meal of barley bread and goat's milk, and while they ate Dick watched his mother, wondering when and how she was going to tell his sisters about their father's death.

"Has Father gone to work, or is he still sleeping?" asked Meg.

The time had come.

"Dick," said his mother, "I'd like to talk to Meg and Beckie on their own. I'm sure you don't want to hear what I have to say."

"I'm going down to the mine," said Dick. "They need all the help they can get."

He moved towards the door and picked up his miner's helmet and string of tallow dips on the way.

His mother handed him a pasty for his croust.

"Dick," his mother called out. He paused. "Dick — ask Cap'n Chegwidden what's to be done."

Dick looked as though he didn't understand.

"You know . . about arrangements and things."

"I'll ask him, mother. Try not to worry."

Dick made his way to the well. It served as the water supply for the cluster of twelve cottages that made up the hamlet of Treen. He pulled off his shirt and tipped a bucket of clear water over the back of his head. It was icy cold and took his breath away. It trickled round to his face and down his back. It was fresh and clean.

He put the string of dips round his neck and the helmet on his head. Then he picked up his shirt and pasty. With water steaming from the warmth of his body, he set off towards Wheal Mary.

He'd walked about a mile when suddenly he was aware of the sound of galloping horses behind him. The sound grew louder, and he stepped aside onto the coarse moorland grass to allow the riders every inch of the rutted track.

Two uniformed soldiers, their white cross-belts bright against their red jackets, bore down on him.

For several fearful seconds he believed that they were after him. They knew of the gold. He and his father had been spotted urging the mule cart with its heavy load

44

away from Portheras Cove. The riders were almost upon him. His mind was numb.

But instead of reining in their mounts as they drew level, the soldiers sped past. A cloud of dust, kicked up by the horses in a mad swirl, now lay in a softly thinning cloud behind them as the thunder of hooves receded.

They weren't after him. He need not have panicked. Yet the fear that had swept through him remained.

In his heart he knew that his business and that of the soldiers was one and the same. Soldiers only passed that way when called to track down wreckers or assist the mine owners in restoring calm, following a riot of desperate and hungry miners, which, nowadays, happened more and more frequently.

Clearly, there was going to be all hell to pay before ten thousand gold pieces were left to benefit those who saw fit to take them from their rightful owner.

The brandy and the saffron could be circulated with fair reward and negligible risk. But how do you spend ten thousand pieces of gold without drawing unwanted attention to yourself and family?

The sight of a dark blue cloak draped over a furze bush jolted Dick's thoughts back to the events of the previous night. He untangled it. He remembered when he'd first held it. He remembered the fear and sadness in the face of the dark haired girl, and how she'd called him a thief and talked of murder. Never had he regarded himself or his father as criminals, until that moment. The thought disturbed him. He imagined her scurrying back after his shouted curse on her father; scurrying so quickly that she'd missed her cloak, lying where Chegwidden had dropped it.

He put on his shirt, folded the cloak carefully over his arm, and set out with a determined step to reach Wheal Mary in time to bid for the pitch his father had been so keen to work.

## Chapter 8

DICK ARRIVED AT WHEAL MARY and made straight for the counthouse. Seventy to eighty men were clustered outside. A small covered balcony at the top of the steps was the focal point for the monthly business of setting.

Dick was no stranger to the ritual of Setting Day. All his mining life Dick's father had been a tributer, which meant he regularly had to use his judgement to bid against his fellow miners for a profitable pitch to work.

Tom had always enjoyed the challenge of Setting Day, which was the day put aside for this purpose. Cap'n Chegwidden did his best to ensure that the setting price offered the tributer a living wage while, at the same time, making a profit for the mine.

Dick had worked at Wheal Mary for two years now. He'd inherited from his father the nose for smelling out the potential value of a lode of tin or copper, but he had never in his life bid for a pitch.

Everything reminded Dick of his father; the sight of the tributers huddled in groups, the snippets of conversation, arguments about the time it would take to replace the beam, and talk of 'poor ol' Tom'. Dick felt the loss of his father more now that he was with other people than when he was on his own.

Promptly at eleven o'clock Cap'n Chegwidden came out onto the balcony with the mine clerk and the two underground captains.

Chegwidden indicated that he wanted silence.

"Before we set the pitches today there are two things you'll want to hear about. Wheal Rose was forced to close down last month owing to the disastrous low price of tin on the market. I have negotiated to buy the beam from their Newcomen engine. Sam Kent has made twenty mules available and the beam will be with us the day after tomorrow.

"Meanwhile, I'm making special payment for a salvage team, drawn from men working level seven and below. These levels are flooded and mining below seven will be impossible till the main pumps are working again. They'll be salvaging what rods and equipment they can from the main shaft. We hope to be in full operation within four to five days.

"Secondly, as you know, poor Tom Tregarrick lost his life in most tragic circumstances. He was on the ladder at the time the lightning struck it. His buryin' will take place the day after tomorrow, in the Fish Cellar at Blystra, at eleven o'clock in the morning. I am sure many will want to pay their respects and I'd ask those of you who knew him to extend a helping hand to his widow and children."

There was a general murmur among the men.

"Now to the task in hand," announced Chegwidden.

The mine clerk handed him a fistful of pebbles and the familiar routine of setting began.

The clerk read aloud the description of work to be done in each pitch, and the number of men to be employed on it during the next month. Each announcement was followed by a bid from one or more of the assembled tributers, indicating the price, per £1 value of ore, that they were prepared to work for. Captain Chegwidden counteracted with a proposal of a lower amount to be paid for the job. The miner usually modified his first bid, and within half a minute an amicable sum was agreed. Cap'n Chegwidden then read out the proposition and tossed one of the pebbles in the air. If there was no other bid by the time the pebble hit the ground, the last bidder was considered to have secured the pitch in question. His name, and those of his companions who were to work it, were entered in the bargain book by the clerk.

Dick listened closely, as pitch after pitch was announced and a bargain struck for each in turn.

At last the clerk announced, "Now the pitch stretching from Goldsworthy shaft so far west as to join James Martin's pitch, from the forty-eight fathom level, as deep as the fifty-two fathom level. Two men needed."

It was the one that Dick's father had been so determined to work.

"Ten shillin'," shouted a voice.

"Seven," called Chegwidden.

"Nine," shouted the voice.

"Seven and six," Chegwidden counteracted.

"Eight shillin' an' sixpence," called the voice, "an' I'll not work for less," the man added with a certain bravado.

"Eight shillings and sixpence I'm bid for the Goldsworthy pitch," said Chegwidden. He paused. He took a pebble from the table. "Eight shillings and sixpence I'm bid."

Dick's throat was dry. It was now or never. Cap'n Chegwidden tossed the pebble in the air. It was falling to the ground and with it fell Dick's last chance.

"Eight shillings!" Dick couldn't believe it was his voice that had called out. A split second later the pebble hit the ground.

All eyes turned towards the late bidder. Chegwidden looked down at Dick.

"Eight shillings I'm bid for the Goldsworthy pitch," he called and took another pebble in his hand.

"He's only a boy," called the original bidder in disgust, unaware that it was Tom's son. "Yer can't give it to a boy. It's man's work an' there ain't a man 'ere will work it for that price."

"I'll work it for eight shillings!" It was Ben Trewan.

"Yer won't get no man ter work with yer at that price an' the pitch needs two," called the first voice angrily.

"I'll work it with the boy," shouted back Ben Trewan. "Come on Cap'n, I've made a fair bid."

"Eight shillings I'm bid for the Goldsworthy pitch," called Chegwidden. He tossed the pebble into the air. To Dick it seemed to take an age to hit the ground, but it did.

The bid had been taken and his name was being written in the book alongside Ben Trewan's. He could have wished for someone else; someone who would not be anxious for him to share his knowledge of where the *Anneke*'s treasure lay hidden.

"Good luck to yer, boy." The words were spoken by Harry Kerrow, Martha's husband.

"Thanks," said Dick. At least he would be working the pitch his father had wanted.

The next pitch had been announced and the setting continued. Dick saw Ben Trewan pushing through the men towards him.

"I knew it was yer father's wish to work the Goldsworthy, so yer'll be doing what he wanted, now won' you?" said Ben. "We must set ourselves up with tools and dips and fuses an' the like, but that can wait for a day or two."

He put his arm round Dick's shoulders and gave him a rough hug.

"Get along then an' tell yer mother the good news. Tell her she's got a man for a son. An' tell 'er I'll be round later to see if there's ought I can do."

Dick turned hastily, and made his way between the ramshackle buildings, where normally an army of women, the bal maidens, dressed the ore. At normal times it was a noisy, sweaty scene of feverish activity, as the women pounded the ore to dust with their heavy hammers. But Setting Day was a holiday and everywhere was silent and empty.

Dick, lost in thought, was passing the corner of the blowhouse, with its piled tin smelting waste, when his arm was suddenly and painfully grabbed.

"'Ullo, Dick, I bin lookin' for yer."

It was Jago Lugg.

## Chapter 9

DICK FOUND HIMSELF pinned against the blowhouse wall with Jago's face so close that he was nauseated by the man's stale breath.

"You told me lies, Dick boy," said Jago, coming straight to the point. "You told Jago a lie."

Although shocked by Jago's sudden appearance, Dick felt strangely calm. "Just because you didn't find it doesn't make me a liar," he said.

Jago released his tight grip but still held firmly to the boy. "Well now, it's just a bit cocky we are is it?" he said. "Perhaps we'd better get clear in our minds what we mean by 'it'! Now, if you mean the haul from the *Anneke*, then the answer's no, I didn't find 'it', but if you're referring to something else in connection with the *Anneke*, then perhaps I did find 'it'!"

Dick thought, frantically. "I told you all I know."

"Did yer now?" said Jago. "Well, I thought there was a bit more to your haul than just a dead body in a coffin."

So the old devil had found the coffin! "You don't scare me!"

"I'm pleased to hear you say that," said Jago, "'cos I'd 'a' thought you 'ad two things to be scared of. The first, on account of you being a party to the killing of a sea-cap'n. And the second on account of you lied to Jago about where you hid the stuff that this poor ol' cap'n was trying so 'ard to protect."

Dick didn't speak.

"Lost yer tongue 'ave yer?"

"No," said Dick boldly. "I haven't anything to say."

It was at that point that Jago noticed the cloak which Dick still carried over his arm. He checked what he was

51

about to say, and put his hand out to touch it. "Where'd you find that?"

"On the trackway, across the moor."

"Whereabouts on the track?"

"What's it to do with you?"

Jago tightened his grip on Dick's arm once more. He spoke slowly and deliberately. "That's my Lizzy's cloak. That's what it's got to do with me, an' I'd like to know where you got it?"

"I told you — on the track...well..."

"Yes?"

"Over a furze bush at the side o' the track, to be exact."

"That's better," said Jago; "it's exactness I want from you."

"Well, if it's your Lizzy's, you'd best take it," said Dick. He thrust the cloak with all his strength into Jago's face. Jago relaxed his grip for just a moment. It was enough. Dick shook his arm free. Jago clawed savagely at the cloak, tearing it from his face, but in the two seconds that this took him, Dick had vanished.

The setting procedure had been completed. Most of the miners had dispersed but three or four groups of men still stood chatting. Cap'n Chegwidden was talking to Harry Kerrow. Dick made straight for the cap'n.

"Aha! There you are Dick Tregarrick," said Chegwidden, turning to see who was panting so hard.

"Good mornin', sir," said Dick.

"So you'll be tacklin' the Goldsworthy inside a week, eh?"

"Yes, sir."

"Is there anything I can do in the meantime?"

"Mother said to ask you about arrangements for Father's buryin'?"

"I've arranged with Harry Kerrow to tell your mother all the details. I'd go myself but with the business of salvaging and getting the pumps working again, I've got to be hereabouts over the next two days."

Dick glanced over his shoulder. There was no sign of Jago.

"Well, I'll be getting along then. Thank you very much for your help, sir," said Dick.

"I'm sure we'll get along well," said Chegwidden.

As Dick turned away from the captain, the clatter of approaching horses' hooves drew his attention towards the entrance of the mine.

It was the soldiers. They reined in their horses and asked one of the miners a question to which the answer was an extended arm and finger pointing in Dick's direction. Dick turned away, and walked as steadily as he could towards the engine house.

Nervously, he glanced over his shoulder. The soldiers were dismounting to talk to the Captain. So it was Chegwidden the miner had pointed to, not him. Dick took a deep breath. He stopped to watch, as all the other men were now doing.

Chegwidden lead the two soldiers towards the count house. One was a sergeant in the Yeomanry, the other a trooper.

On a sudden impulse, Dick decided to find out what they were doing here. After all, they might be on business which had nothing to do with him and the chests of gold from the *Anneke.* He ran over to the three men.

"Can I look after the horses, sir?" His question was addressed to Chegwidden.

"That's kind of you, Dick," said the mine cap'n.

"Thank you, boy. I'm sure they'd like some water and a bite of hay," said the sergeant.

Dick led the horses to the stable, exchanged their bridles for halters, and tied them up, making sure that both hay and water were within their reach. Then he hurried across the yard to the count house.

The mine clerk barred his way as he bounded up the steps.

"Where do you think you're going?" the man asked.

"I'm in charge of the soldiers' horses," said Dick. "I just want to find out if they need a rub down. Can you tell me where the Cap'n's taken the two gentlemen?"

The mine clerk explained where to find the captain and Dick slid inside.

The door of the room was shut. Dick paused outside. He could hear voices.

"This Comte de Valois must be a very important fellow." It was Chegwidden making the observation.

"He's related by marriage to our own King George, and plans are afoot to get him out of France urgently. He stayed on, at great risk to his own life, to ensure that at least some of his wealth was safely put on board the *Anneke*."

Dick started at the name of the *Anneke*. So it was to do with the chests of gold that he and his father had plundered from the wreck!

"This revolution in France is a bad thing," said Chegwidden.

"They're a fiery lot, the French," said the sergeant. "And with hunger in their bellies there's no end to the atrocities the common herd will commit under their champion, Robespierre."

"It's said that no member of the aristocracy is free from the fear of the guillotines," said Chegwidden.

"That's true."

"So what do you want me to do?" said Chegwidden.

"Ploos von Amstel, the captain of the *Anneke*, was acting under direct instructions from the King's Chancellor, Kegwallader, to ensure that the Count's property reached these shores safely. The gold must be found. And we're approaching all responsible, law-abiding men in position of authority, to notify us of any hint of gold being circulated or smelted down."

"They keep tight together these Cornishmen, as you well know," said Chegwidden. "The chances of me hearing anything are remote."

"Do you know of any men who work at Wheal Mary who might've been at Portheras Cove that night?"

"I'd've thought this Captain von Amstel would've been your man to question," said Chegwidden, avoiding the soldier's question.

"There's no trace of him," said the sergeant.

"Then he's your culprit!"

"It'd be more than his life's worth."

"Well, if you've not found him nor his body, and you've not found the gold, there's a good chance he's still around to spend it," said Chegwidden. "I'd feel happier keeping an eye open for a Dutch sea-captain than one o' my own men."

"I appreciate your loyalty to your men, but we must impress upon you that this is no ordinary matter. It's not only His Majesty's Preventive Officers you're up against, it's the King himself and I can promise you this, Cornwall will be torn apart until we . . . ."

"An' what do you think you're doing?"

Dick started. The mine clerk was standing immediately behind him. "I . . . I . . . was just about to knock but . . . ."

"But . . . ?"

"I didn't like to interrupt."

"That's a poor excuse for eavesdropping. Either knock and go in, or get off."

Dick knocked.

"Come in."

"Excuse me, sir. I've fed and watered the horses. I wondered if I was needed any more. I've left the horses in the stables."

"That's fine. You can go," said Chegwidden.

"Thank you, sir."

"Thank you, boy," said the sergeant.

Dick closed the door behind him and walked briskly down the corridor.

He stood on the steps outside and took a deep breath.

The day was still fine, bright, and very hot. He decided to eat his pasty in peace and quiet in the privacy of a small hideout, known only to himself, tucked away in the middle of the nearby moorland. There, he would have time to think, without being disturbed.

## Chapter 10

LIZZY WAS preparing a meal when her father came in.

"You're just in time, father," she said. "Your food is ready."

Jago sat down and put the cloak on the floor, under the table by his feet.

"Where have you been?" asked Lizzy.

"Wheal Mary. It's Setting Day."

"Any work for you?"

"Oh, there'll be work, even for half a man like me. They ain't got 'emselves sorted out yet, after the storm."

"Good. It means you can have a few more days to rest."

"Rest, rest! Plenty o' time for that when they nails me in my coffin."

"Don't talk like that."

"I. . .er. . .I met a friend o' yours."

"Oh! Who was that?" asked his daughter, stirring a large pot of vegetable soup.

"Dick Tregarrick." Jago kept his eye fixed on his daughter. He noticed a sudden stiffening of the girl's body as the stirring stopped for a moment.

"Who?"

"You know — young Dick Tregarrick. Him that was here yesterday evening."

The girl had recovered her composure. "That hardly makes him a friend of mine."

"Well, he seemed very worried about you. Was afraid you might've caught cold," said Jago.

Lizzy stopped stirring the soup and turned to face her father. Jago slowly picked the cloak from the floor and laid it on the table.

"'E was most anxious to return this to you."

"Where'd you find that?" There was an unnatural urgency in her voice.

"Dick Tregarrick give it to me at Wheal Mary. Said would I be kind enough to give it back to my dear Lizzy."

"I've been looking for it, everywhere."

"Well," said Jago, in a very matter of fact and kindly voice. "That's the message an' there's yer cloak."

"Thank you." Lizzy took the cloak from the table and hung it behind the front door. "He must've stolen it from the door when he left last night. He's got a cheek."

"What would Dick want to go stealing a girl's cloak for?" said Jago. "I ask yer?"

"I don't know. Probably shock after the way you treated him. I heard you in there."

"Well, that wasn't his story."

Lizzy placed two bowls of soup on the table and cut two slices from the barley loaf.

"Lizzy, I'm not cross with you."

"Why should you be?" she said indignantly.

"Yer growing into a very 'andsome girl," remarked her father benignly. "Yer'll be attracting the likes of young men like Dick Tregarrick."

"For the last time, I don't know the boy," she shouted at her father, "and I'm not the sort of girl who goes around trying to attract the likes of him."

"What've I said? Now look girl, I want a simple little heart-to-heart with you. Lord, if you haven't got yer poor mother's fire in yer belly. Give me a chance and 'ear me out."

"What are you up to, you old devil, eh?" Lizzy breathed. She was angry, and embarrassed.

"Now Lizzy," said Jago. His voice was firm and calm in contrast to his daughter's emotional outburst. "Sit down. It's time yer knew what yer old father's up against."

Lizzy sat down but pushed the bowl of soup away from her.

"Come on, eat up."

"I don't feel hungry any more."

"All right, just sit and hear me out."

In between mouthfuls of soup and bread, Jago told his daughter how his old friends had refused to share the *Anneke*'s haul with him. He told her how he'd risked his own life on many an occasion to help the likes of Tom and Ben and Maddy, and how unjustly they'd repaid him.

"You saw how they treated me this morning. In me own 'ome! It wouldn't a' happened if dear old Tom 'ad lived," he continued. "There's a cruel 'and o' fate steppin' in against yer old father again. I admit I acted a bit 'asty with young Dick. I should never 'a' brought 'im 'ere, an 'im with his father 'ardly cold."

"No, you shouldn't."

"Anyways, that's all in the past and what's done is done." Jago took a mouthful of soup. "But I can make amends." He continued speaking through a mouthful of food. "Or rather...*we* can make amends."

Lizzy wondered what was coming next.

"You see..." Jago chose his words carefully. "It doesn't matter about me, any more. I'm old enough and sharp enough to look after mesel', but young Dick... young Dick 'e's in need o' a lot o' help."

"To save him from the likes of you, for a start," said Lizzy, sharply.

"Now less o' yer tongue girl." Jago spoke harshly for a moment, then reverted to his softer voice.

"I said I done wrong by 'im and, because I did what I did, 'e ain't gonna let me 'elp 'im... well, not yet awhile, anyway. But he needs help."

In the long pause that followed Jago looked at his

daughter. Lizzy was aware that whatever her father was leading up to was about to come.

"Lizzy, I don't know how Dick 'ad your cloak..." Lizzy opened her mouth to speak but Jago went straight on. "...an' what's more I don't want to know. But, seein' it draped carefully and neatly over 'is arm, it gave me the idea of 'ow I could help 'im." Jago paused. "Through you, Lizzy."

"You're up to something."

"I ain't up to nothing," Jago snapped. "Heaven help us. When you try to do a body a good deed yer own daughter turns against yer."

He pushed his empty dish roughly away from him and stood up. "Lizzy, I'm askin' yer to get to know Dick, make a friend of 'im."

Lizzy said nothing.

"Do yer 'ear what I'm sayin'?"

"Yes."

"Well?"

"Well what?"

"Well, what do yer think of the idea?"

Lizzy was suspicious of her father's sudden interest. "He's a nice boy," she said.

"O' course 'e's nice. That's the 'ole point!" said Jago.

"Is it?"

"Is it what?" Her father was beginning to lose patience.

"Is it the whole point?" Lizzy stared at her father.

"I ain't gonna plead with yer to do a kindly act. I've told yer my mind an' that's the end of it." He stomped into his bedroom, slamming the door behind him.

Lizzy watched him go. She ate. Then, quietly getting up from the table, she walked across to her curtained-off bedroom. She propped a mirror on her pillow, and taking a brush from a small table beside her bed, began to brush her long, dark hair.

Jago paced up and down, smarting under the suspicious comments of his daughter, but hoping that the seeds he'd planted in her mind would grow and bear fruit. It could be a clever way to get the information he wanted from Dick, if only his daughter played her part.

## Chapter 11

DICK'S SPECIAL HIDEOUT was about three quarters of a mile from Wheal Mary. Situated on the outskirts of an ancient Iron-Age settlement, it was a well-concealed *fogou,* a short tunnel, carved through a small hillock and bolstered up with slabs of granite. Half way through was a small chamber leading off to the right.

Normally, Dick hid himself away in this concealed chamber when he wanted to be alone, but today it was too dark and too cool inside. Pleasantly shaded from the blazing sun, he propped himself against the wall just inside the entrance and prepared to enjoy his croust.

There were places like this scattered all over Cornwall. They must have served some purpose, but nobody seemed to know why they'd been built. Some said it was a bolt hole where the ancients would run for protection when attacked. Others felt it was used for some ancient and long since forgotten, mystic rite. Dick favoured the idea that it had been used to store food. The inner chamber certainly kept cool. Even on the hottest day like today there was often a breeze blowing through the tunnel. Whatever the reason for its existence, Dick found it an ideal hideaway.

Now he needed to think over the events of the past two days. Only he knew where the gold was hidden. In a way he relished this thought. It assured his safety at the hands of Jago or Ben or Maddy. While it remained his secret, they wouldn't dare harm him. He was their one chance of finding it. On the other hand he could hardly call himself rich. He couldn't use the gold in its present form without the risk of getting caught.

Dick ate his pasty.

His thoughts wandered to his father's funeral. He

wasn't looking forward to that. He had loved his father dearly and he found it difficult to stop himself thinking of what might have been, had his father lived.

A sudden rustling in the grass just above his head interrupted his thoughts. He stopped eating and sat, motionless. Someone was standing on top of the *fogou*. Dick held his breath. His ears strained to hear the slightest sound. A chink of harness told him that, whoever it was, had come on horseback.

"Over here!" The voice rang out loud and clear, and seconds later as he listened carefully, he heard the thud of hooves as a second rider approached.

"This looks as good a place as any," said the first voice.

Dick froze. It was the soldiers.

"It'll do."

The second man dismounted and flopped to the ground.

"What do you make of it?" It was the sergeant who spoke.

"They're a close knit lot hereabouts an' no mistake."

"We can't rely on any of 'em giving information against their own kind, and that's a fact."

"When they see we mean business someone'll talk."

"We can't hang around waiting for the first informer to save his cowardly skin. The Colonel wants action, and fast."

Dick was well hidden, but he could see the grass moving as one of the grazing horses tugged at it.

He heard the sounds of drinking and eating. Of all the places they could have chosen, the soldiers had settled on this one spot to rest and eat!

He could now see the tip of a muzzle as the horse persisted in cropping the grass, on the very edge of the hole in which he sat, hidden.

"What are we going to do, then?" said the trooper.

"Make a show of force," said the sergeant. "We'll pick on several villages in the neighbourhood and make a house-to-house search. There was brandy and saffron on board the *Anneke* as well as the gold. We might find traces of that."

There was a long pause while the men concentrated on their food and drink.

The horse was now causing such a disturbance at the entrance to the *fogou* that clouds of tiny seeds wafted over Dick. They played around his nostrils and gave him the overwhelming desire to sneeze.

"It might help us if they put out a reward. Every man has his price," said the sergeant.

Dick sneezed. The horse reared away, giving a terrified whinny. Two surprised faces peered down at him. Dick sneezed a second time.

"Bless you," said the sergeant.

"Thank you," said Dick, not moving.

"Well...er...it looks as though we've stumbled on your secret hideout. Come out and join us."

Dick crawled out, clutching the half-eaten pasty in his hand.

"Well, well, well; it's the lad who took care of our horses at the mine. That's right, isn't it?"

"Yes sir."

"What's yer name?"

"Tregarrick, sir — Dick Tregarrick." He sat down and took a bite at his pasty to avoid having to say more.

"I...er... suppose you overheard what we were talking about?"

"I wasn't spying, I often come out here when I want to be quiet. When I heard you ride up I thought I'd better lie low and wait for you to go."

"Of course you weren't spying. We didn't know ourselves where we were going to eat, so you couldn't have known."

He laughed, and the trooper laughed. Dick smiled.

"The problem is;" the sergeant had stopped laughing; "can you keep a secret?"

Dick opened his mouth to speak, but the trooper interrupted him. "More to the point — can we trust you to keep a secret?"

Dick said nothing.

"You see, we were talking about highly confidential matters," said the sergeant.

"You can trust me — honest," said Dick.

The soldiers obviously didn't want the neighbourhood warned of any forthcoming house-to-house search.

"I came out here to get away from everyone. My father was killed yesterday in an accident at the mine. Ask Cap'n Chegwidden — he'll tell you — and I just wanted some peace and quiet to think. No one comes out here, as a rule."

"Oh!" The sergeant paused. "I'm sorry to hear about your father."

"Yes, that's sad," said the trooper, "if it's true."

Dick jumped to his feet and started to walk away. The soldier was on his feet in an instant. He caught Dick by the shoulder and swung him round.

"Where d'you think you're going?"

"Home."

"Not before we say you can go, you don't," said the trooper, pushing Dick back towards the sergeant.

"Leave the boy alone," said the sergeant.

"How do we know he hasn't heard more than's good for 'im?"

"We don't," said the other soldier. "Come here, boy. Let's make sure we understand each other. We don't know if you heard anything we said, but the point is you might've done, eh?"

"My father *was* killed yesterday." Dick looked fiercely at the trooper.

"Look, I'm sorry to hear about your father. You've got enough troubles. But so have we," said the sergeant. "Listen, you could do yourself, and us, a big favour. Did you ever hear of the wrecking of the *Anneke?*"

"Of course I have, everyone's heard of it." Dick decided there was a limit to the amount he could bluff his ignorance.

"Everyone may have *heard* about it, but no one seems to *know* anything about it. What do you know about it, son?"

"What do you mean?" said Dick.

The sergeant took a silver coin from his pocket and tossed it in the air. Taking care to catch it, he held it towards Dick.

"There's plenty more where that came from, boy, if you can give us a name. Just one name. Anyone you think might've been on the beach at the wrecking of the *Anneke.*"

Dick didn't speak immediately. "How much is plenty more?"

The sergeant thought for a moment. "Four," he said. "Four pieces of silver for a name."

"I can give you a name for four pieces of silver."

"Good boy," said the sergeant.

"He could give us any old name," said the trooper. "How we goin' to. . .?"

"Shut up," commanded the sergeant. He turned to Dick again.

"All right, a bargain's a bargain — the name."

"Money first."

The trooper gave a grunt of disgust and turned away. The sergeant took another coin from his pocket.

"Two now, the rest later."

He held them out and Dick took them.

"Right, you can see I'm a man of my word. What's the name, boy?"

"Lugg, Jago Lugg."

"Where can we find him?"

"You didn't say anything about where to find him. You said four coins for a name," said Dick, defiantly.

The trooper took two strides towards Dick and lifted his hand to strike him.

"Leave him!" roared the sergeant; then softening his voice, "No more I did, and that's a fact."

"Can I have my other two pieces?" said Dick.

"As soon as we've checked out this Jago Lugg you'll get your other two pieces."

"I thought you said you were a man of your word," said Dick.

"If you'll tell us where to find him you'll save us a lot of time and get your two pieces much quicker."

"You can pay me when you find him," said Dick. He turned and began to move away.

"Oh! Dick," called the sergeant "— Dick Tregarrick! If you're wasting our time we shall have to take you in."

Dick began to run in the direction of Wheal Mary.

The soldiers watched him go.

## Chapter 12

AS SOON AS DICK made sure no one was following, he turned right from the track that led towards Wheal Mary and made off across the moor in the opposite direction. He felt a strange elation at the plan which had come to him.

He had deliberately given Jago's name to the soldiers, and now he intended to collect several bags of saffron from the hide-out and plant them in and around Jago's cottage. This would arouse enough suspicion in the minds of the soldiers to convince them that Lugg had been involved in the *Anneke* affair.

Tom Tregarrick had always clung to the maxim that 'A ha'p'th o' thoughtful action is worth a sovereign o' bluster.' Dick took after his father, and without consciously realising, he was doing exactly what his father would have done.

With constant checks over his shoulder, he made for the notorious Old Men's Workings.

For centuries the 'old men', as the ancient miners were called, had burrowed away into the cliffs following wherever the precious tin lodes led them. Centuries of haphazard tunnelling had resulted in a labyrinth of underground passageways. Long since fallen into disuse, they now constituted one of the most dangerous places in Cornwall.

Many a tale was told of folk who had entered the Old Men's Workings never to be seen again. Children were forbidden, and men feared, to go near there.

Apart from the physical danger of getting lost, there was also the superstition that the place was haunted by spirits of men, long since departed and doomed for eternity to search in vain for a way out. Even the most hardened smuggler or wrecker shunned the place. Where better to hide the haul of a lifetime?

An uncharted labyrinth of underground passages and rumoured spirits had not been enough to deter Tom Tregarrick. Nowhere could a fortune lie so secretly and securely.

"All we need is a code — and the simpler the better," Tom had said to his son, as they guided the mules towards the Old Men's Workings on the night of the *Anneke.* Let's make it twos . . . and right and left alternate, eh boy? We choose the opening, take the second tunnel on the right and then second on the left, then second on the right and so on. We can't get lost. Coming out we just reverse it."

As Dick approached the workings he made a last check over his shoulder before moving up to the gaping entrance.

Once there, he paused only to light one of his dips. Then, fixing it to his miner's helmet, he stepped into the mouth of the largest tunnel.

He took the second tunnel on the right and the blackness closed in behind him. The walls glistened with water. Second left. He recalled that night when he and his father had trod this same pathway dozens of times. First they had carried the chests of gold, then the kegs of brandy, and last of all the saffron. Second right. He recalled the intense excitement he had felt. The whole operation had taken the best part of half an hour and yet it was now a feverish blur in his memory. Every muscle in his body had ached, but he had been determined to show his father that he could keep up with him. Second left. Only a few paces and he took the second right again. The fat from the dip dribbled onto the ball of clay which held it. He moved quickly and sure-footedly. He didn't stop to think of the maze of tunnels that surrounded him. Second left. The tunnels swelled and narrowed, bearing witness to the uneven lodes which had long since been carved out. Second right, and he was there.

It was the end of the tunnel. This must be the place. Dick stared in disbelief. There was nothing. No brandy, no saffron, no gold — nothing.

He was gripped by sudden panic. He had taken a wrong turning! It was the wrong tunnel. It had to be.

"Father!"

The sudden echo of the word he uttered frightened him even more. Why he'd called out at all he didn't know. The echo died and Dick stood, alone. A gentle plop of water dripped from the crack above onto his helmet.

As suddenly as the panic had seized him, it went. He had stood on this very spot before. Droplets of water had fallen on to his helmet then, as he had stood there to regain his breath after carrying a heavy chest of gold. They'd carried it between them, and Tom had paused several times on the way to allow his son to take a breath.

'Come on boy, yer head'll turn mildew, if yer stand there much longer.'

"I'm ready, Father!" Dick actually spoke his part of the conversation out loud. The sound of his voice shocked him back to reality. He examined the wall to his right. Above his head to the right it had been — just above his head. He stopped. He'd found what he was looking for. There, just above head height and to the right was a narrow ledge of rock. On the ledge was a ball of clay in which his father had stuck a dip to light the tunnel. He'd lit two!

Dick retraced his steps — three — four — five. He found it. This time the clay had been stuffed into a crack by his father and far from burnt out — the dip still clung to the wall beneath the clay.

This was the place. He was not lost.

Then where was the stuff?

Dick found himself breathing hard, almost panting. He forced himself to breathe more steadily. Where in God's name was it?

A small trace of yellow powder on the floor attracted his eye. He knelt and examined it. Saffron, spilled from a split bag. If he needed more proof that he was in the right spot that was it.

'Only Father, and me knew where it was.' His eyes stared in fear. 'It's been spirited away.'

The thought was insane, but he could not rid himself of it. He had to get out. He turned. His mind grappled with the code. Which way had he come in? He had to set off correctly or he'd never get out.

He turned left.

'Yes, left that's it — left, because I turned right into the tunnel.'

God, how he wanted to get out. Second right. His heart beat fast as his footsteps echoed. Second left. He'd have to tell someone now, he'd have to. Surely he would be able to see the glimmer of daylight soon, any moment now. Second right. For one terrifying moment he thought he'd taken a wrong turning.

Second left.

'O God, please let it be the right way!'

He looked back to recall the last direction he'd turned.

'If I don't see daylight within the next turn or two I'm done for.'

He moved on, his eyes searching ahead for that glimmer that would mean safety. He thought he could see it. He was approaching the second turning to his right. He turned. He took a deep breath. The blackness that had surrounded him was giving way to daylight. He broke into a run. The sudden draught caused by his quick movement blew out his dip, but it didn't matter. The tunnel was getting lighter, lighter. He turned left and burst out of the tunnel into glorious warm, welcoming sunshine. He didn't stop for breath; he kept on running, up towards the moorland. At last he stopped running, but continued to walk at a fast pace. He was gasping for breath, but he kept moving.

He was on the moor. He had a clear view for miles around. He gulped in the air as his heart slowed to a more tolerable beat.

His mind was confused. In the reassuring light of day, he found it difficult to believe that solid kegs and chests could have been spirited away. But who? Who?

Jago Lugg's cottage was about two miles away.

Without stopping to reason or consider the danger, he quickened his pace towards the cottage, which lay in a hollow over the brow of the hill.

'It couldn't be Jago.' He'd seen him only a few hours ago. The wild thought flashed through his mind that he must talk to Lizzy again. He wasn't sure what about or why. He had to talk to someone. But why Lizzy?

He breasted the rise and looked down into the valley below.

As his eyes searched for the cottage they were drawn to the track that stretched beyond; the track that led from Wheal Mary to Lugg's cottage.

Riding from the direction of the mine towards the cottage were the two soldiers. It had taken them less than an hour to discover where Jago lived.

## Chapter 13

THE SIX COFFIN BEARERS sweated uncomfortably under the weight of their dead load. Dick walked with his mother and Meg behind the coffin. Old Mrs Kerrow had stayed at home to care for John and Beckie. Ruth Tregarrick stared ahead trying not to think of Tom's dead body lying in that box.

The long procession of neatly-dressed mourners wound back for several hundred yards. Every one of them could tell a tale connected with Tom Tregarrick. If Dick had cared to count them he would probably have stopped at two hundred and still there were more. But Dick didn't count them. For him, the whole burying process seemed unreal. He was aware of the dull melody they sang, scores of voices, joining in harmony. He longed for the day to end.

The procession wound slowly towards the fish cellar, perched above the tiny harbour of Blystra.

The hamlet of Treen, where the Tregarricks lived, did not boast a chapel, nor a resident preacher. The only place for communal gatherings was the fish cellar at Blystra.

The folk of Blystra relied upon catching pilchards for a living and the focal point of the village, indeed of the whole district, was the fish cellar. It was a long, low, two-storied timbered building. The bottom half was used for the storage of the fishermen's legitimate bounty from the sea, while the upper half was reserved for community gatherings. It was the one place that could accommodate the visiting preacher, a coffin, and a reasonable number of mourners.

It was May, and the bulk of last season's catch had long since left the Cornish coast bound for Catholic tables round the Mediterranean shores. Even so, many a barrel of pilchards remained, oozing gallons of precious oil to fill the villagers' lamps during the dark nights.

The lingering smell of oily fish filtered through the cracks in the floor from the ground below.

The preacher droned on about sin and the devil, and repentance of sins and life after death. Altogether Dick wasn't sure what the man meant, but presumably repentance meant being so sorry for doing wrong that you were allowed to live forever somewhere high above the clouds.

At that moment he wanted to believe the preacher, for his father's sake, except that his poor father had had no time to repent. He wasn't expecting to die. Does one ever expect to die?

Dick's rambling thoughts were jolted back to the fish cellar. The preacher had stopped talking, and the six bearers were struggling to lift the coffin onto their shoulders for its final journey to the graveyard.

Dick was grateful to be in the fresh air again. His eyes scanned the local cliff tops, anxious to see as far away as possible from the dismal scene that hemmed him in.

Seagulls wheeled and screamed overhead. The humid haze of the morning was giving way to a clear blue sky. Dick wanted to shake off the confused feelings which gnawed at him. If only he could break away and run along those cliff tops with the breeze, fresh in his face, free as the air around him, free to . . . He stopped dead in his tracks. He stopped so suddenly that Ben, walking behind, bumped into him.

"Come on boy — not much further to go. Bear up," murmured Ben, comfortingly.

Dick moved forward again, his eyes searching along the cliff tops, desperate to catch another glimpse of the sight which had made him stop so suddenly.

There was nothing.

For an unbelievable moment he had thought he had seen a man standing on the cliff top; a man whose stance and stature were identical to his father's. His emotions were playing tricks on his eyesight. For one powerful heartbeat, Dick could have sworn that he had seen his father, standing on the cliffs above them.

The coffin was lowered into the ground and the first symbolic spadefuls of earth were sent splattering on top of it.

That really was the end. The preacher had been at great pains to assure everyone that this was not the end, but Dick was unable to imagine anything more final than the scene in front of him.

The realisation that he would never see his father again forced out the tears that strained to be released.

The ceremony was over. The mourners stood in groups, talking in low voices. Captain Chegwidden came over to his mother and drew her to one side. Dick felt vaguely embarrassed, and resentful at being excluded from whatever it was the mine captain had to say.

Suddenly he noticed a lone figure, some hundred yards from him. It was Lizzy. Dick moved towards her. As he approached, he noticed that her large dark eyes were red-rimmed and her cheeks wet with tears. He'd no idea that the death of his father could have affected her so greatly.

"It's good of you to come," he said quietly.

"Why do you say that?" said the girl, coldly. She wiped her cheeks with the back of her hands.

"I didn't know you knew my father," said Dick.

"I didn't," said Lizzy. There was a trace of bitterness in her voice.

"Then why are you here?"

"My father's been taken to Truro gaol. I've been at my wits' end for over a day now. I've no one to turn to."

"Taken to Truro gaol . . . but why?"

Dick was genuinely surprised. Although he had given Jago's name to the soldiers he'd been unable to plant any incriminating evidence. On what pretext could they have taken him?

"Two soldiers came. They searched the house, and when they found nothing, they searched my father." Lizzy paused. "They found some papers on him which belonged to the captain of the *Anneke*."

Dick stared at the girl. So, Jago had found the captain's body. He must have done. And taken the captain's papers! His father had expressly forbidden Ben and Maddy to take anything from the body.

"The whole idea is to make people believe that the cap'n's up and gone with the gold," he'd said. "Any hint that someone's been through his pockets will leave him above suspicion and they'll come looking for us. Don't touch him!" Dick could see the expression on his father's face as he'd spoken the words there at Portheras Cove.

"The solders tried to make my father confess, and tell where he'd hidden the stuff he'd taken from the *Anneke*," said Lizzy.

"Did he tell them?" said Dick.

"How could he? He had nothing to do with the wrecking. I told them he'd been on his sick bed. They asked how he'd come by the captain's papers and he said he'd discovered the captain's body down the shaft at Lower Gun."

The girl's eyes searched Dick's face for a sign that he understood what she was talking about. "They wanted names of people who'd been at Portheras that night."

"What did he say?"

"He said there was one person who could tell them everything."

Dick returned the girl's gaze. Outwardly he looked calm but his mind was in a frenzy. "Did he say who that person was?"

"You. That's who he said could tell them everything. You — Dick Tregarrick."

Dick turned abruptly and walked quickly towards his mother.

"You've got to help me!" The girl's cry barely reached him.

# Chapter 14

SAM KENT had kept his word. While Tom Tregarrick's body was being buried, the vital beam from Wheal Rose had been hauled to Wheal Mary by Sam's mules.

Next morning, the area round the engine house was a hive of activity as men worked to install the new beam.

Dick had barely slept. His mind wandered from the sight of the clods of earth, which had slowly covered his father's coffin, to the fear of being awoken by soldiers battering the door down. Now he searched for Ben. He needed a friend.

Ben was deep in conversation with Harry Kerrow. The two men were standing at the entrance to the surface level when Dick saw them.

"Here comes my new partner," said Ben, smiling.

"Mornin' Dick," said Harry.

"Mornin' Mr Kerrow, mornin' Uncle Ben."

"I think from today we can drop the 'uncle'," said Ben. "I reckon we're equal partners now, eh?"

Dick smiled, slightly embarrassed.

"Harry is taking over my job as sumpman, now that I'll be working the Goldsworthy," said Ben, "and you and I, Dick boy, must buy the tallows and fuses we need, so we don't waste a minute from the moment the pitch is pumped and..."

"I must speak to you." Dick's interruption was harsher and louder than he'd intended. He was bursting to tell Ben of the fearful problem that weighed him down. He was afraid.

"You feelin' all right, Dick?"

"I must speak to some... to you. It's urgent."

"I'll be leaving then," said Harry. "See you later Ben."

Both men sensed there was something wrong.

"Follow me Dick. I know a place where we won't be interrupted."

Dick followed Ben into the level towards the top of the shaft.

"We'll just climb down to the first level," said Ben, lighting a dip and fixing it to his helmet. "I know a nice little hidey hole."

Dick clambered down the ladder after Ben. He remembered the excitement he'd felt when last he'd climbed down after his father. His whole world had changed since then.

Within two minutes, Dick found himself in a tiny man-made cave, just big enough for two people. Someone had obviously put some work into it to make it comfortable. It had a small table fixed on a two-foot high length of timber. Two small off-cuts from prop timbers served as stools.

Ben winked at Dick as he fixed the dip to a lump of clay on the wall. "Regular 'ome from 'ome, eh Dick?"

"Is it yours?"

"Well yer might say that — in a manner of speaking. Yer see a sumpman 'as a sort of rovin' job — up and down and around. No 'ome to go to — not like the tributers 'oled up in their pitches — so I adopted this little place. I comes here to eat my croust," he said, placing a pasty on the table, "to have a smoke," he added, taking out his clay pipe and tobacco, "and to listen to others when they're in trouble." He looked straight at Dick. His hands automatically filled and lit his pipe.

Dick came straight to the point.

"It's about the *Anneke*. The soldiers have got my name."

Ben stared at him through a haze of tobacco smoke. "How do yer know?"

Words tumbled from Dick's mouth as he told Ben everything. How he'd made it his business to find out why the soldiers had come. How he'd been discovered, listening to their plans at the *fogou*. How, on the spur of the moment, he had given them Jago's name. Ben raised his eyebrows. And how he'd intended to plant some saffron at Jago's cottage to get him out of the way. He told Ben how the soldiers had acted so promptly that he'd not had time to plant the evidence, but they'd found the captain's documents on Jago's person and that was proof enough for them that Jago had something to do with it.

"How do yer know they found the captain's papers on him?"

"His daughter, Lizzy, told me. She also said Jago had given them my name."

Ben sat deep in thought.

"You said . . . yer went to get some saffron to leave at Jago's place. When yer saw the soldiers yer knew yer were too late . . ." Ben paused. "What did yer do with the saffron?"

"I didn't have any."

"Look, Dick, you've got to be straight with me. If the soldiers have got yer name and they find saffron at your place when they come nosing round — 'cause make no mistake they will — then yer done for. No proof and yer got a chance. What did yer do with it, Dick?"

"I didn't get any."

"You went back to the hideout?"

"Yes."

"But you didn't get any?"

"No."

"Why not?"

"The stuff had gone!"

Ben bit hard into the clay stem of his pipe. It snapped. He spat the broken end from his mouth and leant across the table, not taking his eyes off Dick for a second. "What do yer mean — the stuff had gone?"

Dick told him about the Old Men's Workings, the code — everything.

Ben sat back thoughtfully. He relit his shortened pipe and once again the tiny cave was filled with smoke.

"Well . . ." he said at last, and shuffled himself into a more comfortable position, "it certainly ain't no good brooding over where the haul went, or how rich we might have been — though I can tell yer I knew we'd struck it rich this time, and I don't intend to let it disappear just like that, without a deal of thought and effort to find it. But . . . the main thing is that you and me and Maddy don't hang for somethin' we haven't got, leastways, not at the moment."

"Do we have to tell Maddy?"

"I reckon we do. He certainly won't rest until he knows where the haul is — or was, and if Jago did find the captain's body, then it's one o' Maddy's coffins he's got hidden at Lower Gun. It's up to you, me and Maddy to find it before the soldiers. If we destroy that — then there's no evidence linking Maddy, you, and me with the *Anneke*, and Jago's word'll have no proof behind it. With that worry off our backs we'll keep a keen eye open for them who's pinched it. Though it beats me who'd 'a' stumbled across it in the Old Men's Workings without knowing exactly where to look. That really beats me."

A plan was made. Dick was to set off at once to find Maddy and tell him why it was vital to find and destroy the coffin that Jago had found. He was to meet Ben and Dick at Lower Gun that evening at eight o'clock.

In the meantime, Ben would have to make sure that Harry knew all about the job he was to take over at Wheal Mary.

Dick and Ben clambered to the surface and walked along the level towards the rectangle of daylight.

"Right. Yer know what to do then," said Ben. "If I don't see yer before I'll see yer at Lower . . ."

He broke off suddenly. He had just stepped outside into the daylight. Dick was behind him. Ben suddenly leapt back into the level, grabbed Dick and dragged him back into the tunnel three or four paces.

"Soldiers!" he said. "A dozen of 'em at least. You nip back to the hidey hole. Don't come out until I tells yer it's all clear. Here, take this." Ben handed him the helmet and some dips. "Quick, run, boy."

Dick turned and ran. He scuttled down the ladder and didn't stop moving until he threw himself, gasping for breath, into the tiny cave. If only he'd confided in Ben earlier. If only . . .

'It ain't a mite of use wasting yer time on "if only's."' He could hear his father saying it as if he was standing next to him.

Dick folded his arms on the table and rested his head on them. Thought after thought tumbled in his mind until at last, exhausted, worn out from his night of wakefulness and fear, he fell asleep.

When he awoke the dip had burnt out and everything around him was pitch black. He was stiff, cold, and hungry. He couldn't light another dip because Ben hadn't given him anything to light it with. He moved himself into a more comfortable position and tried to stretch his limbs.

The blackness was thick; not the merest hint of light penetrated his underground blindness. He dared not grope his way around the mine in the blackness which engulfed him. He was trapped until someone chose to return to him.

## Chapter 15

DICK HAD LOST all sense of time. He had no idea how long he'd sat there, hardly daring to move, terrified of what might be happening above him at that very moment, if the soldiers had called at his home or found the coffin and arrested Ben. Then, above the distant noise of rushing water he heard the sound of approaching footsteps. They were not the sure heavy footsteps of someone who knew where they were going. They were hesitant, and stopped every now and again, as if the person was uncertain of the way.

Dick froze. They were not Ben Trewan's footsteps.

A glimmer of light showed at the entrance to the cave.

"Dick!" A soft, tentative call, a girl's voice.

The light grew brighter. "Dick!"

Dick stood up. "I'm over here."

Suddenly the hide-out was full of light.

He blinked. Standing in the entrance to the cave was Lizzy. "Ben sent me."

"Why...what's happened?"

"Listen carefully," said Lizzy. "The mine has been teeming with soldiers all day. That's why Ben hasn't been back to see you. He's gone to find Maddy. He told me to wait until the soldiers left, then fetch you. We were to meet him and Maddy at Lower Gun at eight o'clock but it's gone nine already...."

"Gone nine!"

"The soldiers left half an hour ago. I had to make sure they weren't coming back," explained Lizzy. "We must hurry."

She turned and moved off down the tunnel. Dick scrambled out of the cave and hurried to catch up. Lizzy now moved at such a pace it was impossible to talk.

They climbed the ladder. Lizzy was exceptionally nimble and Dick found himself panting to keep up with her.

At the entrance to the level Lizzy blew out the dip, and they peered out cautiously.

A loud hammering came from the engine house and lights glowed in the windows. A small group of men still toiled to get the beam in position.

Everywhere else was dark and still. There was a pale moon, and once their eyes had grown accustomed to the meagre light, Dick and Lizzy set off at a fast pace.

They hugged the deep shadow of the buildings for as long as they could, then as Lizzy made for the main entrance to the mine, Dick stopped her.

"This way," he said. Lizzy followed.

Dick knew the surface layout of the mine well, and there were safer ways of getting clear of the mine without being seen.

It was not until they were well across the moor, heading for Lower Gun, that Dick was able to find some answers to the questions in his mind.

"I was desperate to get help," said Lizzy. "I knew Ben Trewan was a man whom my father had come to trust more than anyone else — so I came to the mine to find him. There were soldiers everywhere!"

"What happened?"

"Ben said he knew about my father, and the soldiers, and that if I helped him, he'd help me. He told me that, once he'd made sure the soldiers couldn't find the coffin, he'd tell them my father had been ill and couldn't have been at Portheras on the night of the *Anneke*. I had to find someone who'd speak up for him."

Dick was struck by the sincerity of the girl and frightened by her despair. He was suddenly filled with an overwhelming desire to be rid of his part in this terrible business.

He wished he'd had the courage to walk away from Portheras on that dreadful night. But Tom had wanted him there, and he had been anxious to make his father proud of him. It was too late to walk away now.

"I'll do what I can to help as well," Dick promised. "It's not right for your father to be in Truro Gaol for somethin' he didn't do."

"Oh thank you — thank you," said the girl.

Her gratitude made him feel strangely calm, although he didn't know why. It didn't alter things. They'd all be lucky to escape with their lives. But after days of confusion, suddenly he saw more clearly what he must do.

They could now see the majestic stack of the engine house at Lower Gun rising black in the distance against the paler night sky.

"Whereabouts at Lower Gun did Ben say he'd meet us?" asked Dick.

"Entrance to the main shaft."

They stumbled on. Their legs now felt the exhaustion from the effort they'd made to reach Lower Gun as quickly as possible. Their breathing was so heavy it filled their ears.

"Stop— right— there!" The command was completely unexpected.

Lizzy stopped. Dick acted instinctively. He grabbed the girl by the arm and jerked her off the track to the left.

"Keep down and follow me." The instruction was crisp and confident.

Dick let go her arm. Bent double, he was pounding his way through low furze. Lizzy had gathered her skirts above her knees and was trying desperately to keep up with him. Needle sharp bristles whipped her face, legs and arms.

They were aware of shouts behind them.

"Stop!"

"Look — over there!"

A sharp explosion was followed by a sickly tearing sound which ripped through the bushes to their right. Almost immediately another explosion was followed by a similar ripping sound to their left. Whoever was firing had an accurate aim. He could only be using the sound of crashing undergrowth to guide his shots.

Dick turned left, took six or seven paces then turned again to confuse the marksman.

The next shot cut through the furze well to their right. They were now fifty yards away. The bushes completely covered their tracks. Two more shots were fired into the bushes. They fell harmlessly away to their right.

"Stop firing! Fan out!" The command echoed clearly through the night air.

Dick and Lizzy scrambled on, frantically. The shock of the ambush had produced untold reserves of energy in their tiring limbs. The darkness, which had helped the soldiers lying in wait, now favoured the quarry.

There were now a hundred yards between hunter and hunted. Dick stopped and a second later Lizzy came level with him. The soldiers were moving slowly and cautiously. Their shouts and curses rang out as they blustered through the furze and stubbed their boots against the haphazardly-strewn blocks of granite.

"We'll be all right," Dick gasped for breath. "I know where we are. We'll just get our breath . . . and then . . . we'll make for Blystra. There's no track. The soldiers won't know which way we've gone."

"What about Ben?"

"It's every man for himself. They've either got him or he's lying low. We should've guessed the soldiers would be at Lower Gun. That was the one lead they must have got from your father. That's where he found the coffin."

A shout from one of the soldiers reminded them they had no more time to waste.

After another hundred yards of darting across the countryside in a doubled position, Dick reckoned they could walk upright, with little chance of being spotted. It was more comfortable and they could move more quickly.

"We'll cut down through Blystra and then up to Ben's place," said Dick.

They walked on briskly for half a mile, in silence.

"I don't know whether it's safe for me to go home or not," said Lizzy.

"I'm sure it's not safe for me," said Dick. "We'll work something out — don't worry."

Dick had found a new strength in himself. He certainly felt more able to cope since he'd taken Ben into his confidence, and it felt good to have a companion in Lizzy.

They soon picked up the lights twinkling from the cluster of fishermen's cottages at Blystra. Ben Trewan lived half a mile the other side. Dick knew the way well. It took them by the graveyard where his father lay buried. He was not anxious to be reminded about the events of the previous day, but there was no other way to go.

Ten minutes later they reached Blystra. Dick guided Lizzy past the fish cellar and out along the track which skirted the graveyard. No other living soul was to be seen.

As they drew level with the graveyard Dick stopped.

"What's the . . . ?" Lizzy began.

Dick cupped his hand over the girl's mouth.

"Sssh! I heard somethin'."

He was about to move on when he heard the sound again. Lizzy heard it too. She gripped Dick's arm. "What is it?" she whispered.

Dick said nothing. His heart pounded against his ribs. He strained his ears to identify the sound.

"Ghosts!"

"Don't be silly," Dick whispered.

They stared at each other in the dim light. The sky was awash with clouds scudding across the face of the moon.

The sound continued. A rhythmic clunk of metal followed by a faint rasping noise.

"It's someone diggin'; in the graveyard!" said Dick.

"At this time of night! Let's leave it. It's none of our business," said Lizzy.

"The noise is comin' from the far corner — near where my father's buried. We can't just leave it," said Dick. "You stay here. I'll be back."

"I'd rather come with you," said Lizzy.

"Don't make a sound," whispered Dick.

Ducking low, they made their way silently around the outer wall of the graveyard.

## Chapter 16

DICK AND LIZZY moved quickly and softly. Every few seconds the rhythmic sound of digging would stop, only to begin again with renewed vigour.

They were as near as they could get now, without entering the graveyard. Dick beckoned Lizzy to keep low. Cautiously he peered over the wall.

The glow of a shielded lantern, helped by the intermittent brightness of the moon, revealed everything. The sounds were coming from his father's grave. Someone was digging out the fresh earth which, only hours before, had been shovelled in to cover his father's coffin.

The man had his back to them. He was already four or five feet down into the grave. Standing several yards from the grave was a mule. Two large panniers were slung from its back, one on either side.

"What's going on?" It was Lizzy.

Dick ducked down behind the wall.

"Someone's diggin' up my father's grave!" The tone of Dick's voice told clearly of the shock he felt.

Lizzy gasped. "Who is it?"

"I don't know," whispered Dick. "He looks familiar, but I can't see his face."

"Let me look," breathed Lizzy.

"All right, but be careful."

Lizzy peered above the wall but ducked down almost immediately.

"He's turned round," she whispered excitedly, her large, dark eyes alive with excitement. "I know who it is."

"Who . . . who?"

"It's Maddy Maddocks!"

Dick peered over the wall.

Lizzy was right. It was Maddy.

"What on earth is he up to?" said Lizzy.

"I don't know, but whatever it is, he can't be up to much good." Dick paused. "Digging up my father's grave!" His tone was one of horror and disgust.

"What shall we do?"

"We'll have to split up," said Dick. "You go to Ben's place as fast as you can. If he's there, tell him what's happenin' and bring him back quickly."

"What if he's not there?" whispered Lizzy anxiously.

"Come straight back. I'll keep an eye on Maddy."

Crouching low, Lizzy slunk off in the shadow of the graveyard wall. Dick knew she'd be gone for some time. He prepared himself for a lonely vigil.

The digging went on.

The night air turned fresh and Dick felt cold. A sudden clunk, as Maddy's shovel hit the top of the wooden coffin, took Dick's mind off his own discomfort and back to the activity in the graveyard.

Soon the sound of frantic scraping of metal on wood indicated that Maddy was clearing the earth from the top of the coffin. Maddy was completely hidden in the grave now and Dick decided it was safe to keep a more constant watch.

Suddenly, the shovel was tossed out of the hole. It landed with a clatter a few feet from the mule. The animal reared and edged away. This was followed by the noise of creaking timber. Dick could not believe his ears. Maddy was levering open the lid of his father's coffin.

Dick's impulse was to leap the wall there and then and put a stop to this sickening, dreadful act. Instead, he clenched his fists until his finger nails bit deeply into the palms of his hands.

A final crack of splintering wood rent the air. Then all fell eerily silent. For half a minute nothing happened. Then came the sound of scrambling and loose dirt falling onto wood. Maddy heaved himself out of the hole. He walked over to the mule, took a length of rope from one of the panniers and led the animal nearer to the grave. Tying one end of the rope to the harness, he lowered the other end into the hole and jumped down. The sound of heavy grunting, as the man struggled to lift something weighty, continued for several minutes. Then Maddy scrambled out of the grave again. He moved over to the mule's head, and taking the bridle, led the animal away from the graveside.

The rope took the strain of the weight to which it was tied. Slowly the object was hauled to the surface. Dick strained his eyes to discover what it could be.

An owl screeched. Dick instinctively ducked down behind the wall.

When he next looked, his eyes could only stare in amazement. Maddy was bending over the object, untying the rope. It was one of the chests containing the gold coins.

Dick's heart pounded.

Maddy repeated the whole operation again. In three or four minutes a second chest lay on the edge of the grave.

Dick could not believe what was happening. If these chests were being raised from the coffin then . . . where was his father's body?

There were now three chests on the ground and still no sign of Lizzy or Ben.

The fourth chest was hauled to the surface to join the other three, and two minutes later it was all over. Maddy had loaded two chests in each of the panniers, extinguished his lantern, and was preparing to lead the mule away.

There was no question of Dick waiting for Lizzy now. He must not lose sight of Maddy. He had to find out where he was taking the gold.

Maddy led the mule out of the graveyard gate at the opposite side to where Dick crouched, behind the wall.

After one last despairing look in the direction from which Lizzy and Ben would come, Dick leapt over the wall and moved quickly to his father's grave.

His eyes tried to pierce the black depths, to see what was left, yet dreading to see his father's corpse lying there uncovered. A shaft of moonlight gave him the light he needed. There, at the bottom of the grave, his father's coffin lay open for all to see. It was empty.

## Chapter 17

MADDY COULD SCARCELY believe his luck. He had taken a great risk and, against tremendous odds, he had succeeded.

"God, 'ave I bin lucky!" he chuckled to himself.

Only two people had known that the gold was in Tom Tregarrick's coffin. Now only one person would know where it was. He gave the mule an elated slap and it quickened its pace.

"I know just the place to stow this tidy fortune — just the place. An' when all the noise 'as died down . . . when everyone has done fussin' and worryin' about it . . ."

A sharp crack of a twig behind him jerked him from his reverie. He halted the mule and turned, straining his eyes to search the darkness. The mule began to move forward again. Maddy yanked it back.

"Sssh! . . . Sssh! . . . damn yer. Be still!"

He listened. He looked.

Dick lay flat and still against the low embankment by the side of the track, some thirty yards behind. He hadn't seen the dead branch on which he'd trodden.

Maddy was walking back towards him. Dick froze. The man stopped ten paces from him. He stood, listening. Dick prayed that the moon would stay behind the clouds.

Maddy, satisfied that there was no one there, turned, strode up to the mule and gave it a resounding slap on its rump.

"Come on ol' girl!"

By now Dick was sure that Maddy was heading for Lower Gun. He was not anxious to go that way. He felt certain there would still be soldiers there, waiting.

Dick crept out from the embankment and moved stealthily after him.

Maddy approached the track that turned off towards Lower Gun. Dick was fifty yards behind him when a tremendous scuffling ahead made him stop dead in his tracks. A startled cry mingled with harsh clanking of the mule's harness and stamping of hooves. Maddy was rooted to the spot in terror, as shadowy figures leapt from the bushes and surrounded him. He found himself looking straight into the barrel of a musket, his arms pinned behind him by someone who was clearly no newcomer to physical violence. Maddy's luck had run out.

"Name?" barked the soldier who held the musket.

"Maddocks." His voice was little more than a hoarse whisper. Beads of perspiration stood out on his forehead.

"Where are you going?"

"Home." Even to Maddy his answer lacked the ring of truth.

"See what he's got in those panniers." The order came from the man who gripped his arms.

One of the soldiers had lit a lantern. He moved over to inspect the contents of the panniers.

Maddy felt a slight easing of the grip on his arms. He wrenched himself free, taking his captor completely by surprise, and plunged desperately into the nearby bushes. The soldier holding the musket swung the weapon in the direction of the escaping man and fired. There was a cry of agony and crash of a body falling.

Dick decided not to wait a moment longer. Maddy was shot, probably dead, for all he knew, and the soldiers had got the gold. That was that. Moving silently and carefully, Dick retraced his steps. When he was sure he was out of earshot, he ran. He decided to make straight for Ben's cottage.

The sky was now overcast, and as he approached the track to Blystra, the first few splashes of rain spattered against his face. He felt that if he didn't eat or rest soon, he would die.

He could run no more. As the track wound down the hill into Blystra, he kept up a fast walking pace, but as it curved slightly uphill past the graveyard, he was forced to slow down.

The rain fell steadily, cold but refreshing. It bathed the scratches on his face and hands where he had forced a way through the furze and undergrowth for himself and Lizzy.

He glanced across the graveyard. A flicker of light caught his eye. At first he thought it must come from a window beyond the graveyard, but there were no cottages beyond. The light moved.

A strong wind now swept the rain full into his face as he screwed up his eyes in an effort to see the light more clearly.

Once again he was scurrying in the shelter of the graveyard wall. In spite of hunger and tiredness, curiosity drove him on.

As he turned the corner, still bent double, he stopped. What if the soldiers were investigating the grave? His heart missed a beat at the thought. He peered cautiously over the wall. The rain made it difficult to see what was happening. As far as he could make out, the light came from a lantern standing on the mound of earth that Maddy had dug from his father's grave. There was no sight nor sound of anybody.

It struck him that Maddy must have left his lantern there. Perhaps he hadn't noticed it before. Then he remembered how he'd stood by the side of the grave waiting for the moon to reveal his father's empty coffin. If the lantern had been there he would have seen it.

Dick moved on stealthily to the place from where he had watched Maddy. Cautiously he looked over the wall.

The rain pattered on the wall in front of him. He could hear nothing but the rain.

He was gripped by a dreadful fear. He wanted to carry on his way to the warmth and shelter of Ben's cottage, but he could not tear himself away.

He slunk down behind the wall and sat with his back against it. He clasped his knees up to his chest and rested his chin on them, barely noticing the rain which now tumbled over him, drenching him to the skin.

When he next looked over the wall, the lantern still burned brightly and there was still no one about. Summoning all his courage, Dick heaved himself to the top of the wall, jumped down on the other side and began to walk, slowly, towards the grave.

He was half way between the wall and the grave when it happened.

Two hands reached out of the grave and fumbled along the edge searching for a firm grip. Dick stopped. He couldn't move. His eyes stared at the hands. In a flurried scramble their owner leapt out of the hole. His boots clawed at the steep sides to give him the final thrust he needed.

Dick's whole body shook, uncontrollably.

There, on his hands and knees at the edge of the hole, the glow of the lantern full upon his face, knelt Tom Tregarrick. The man stared back in alarm at his son's shadowy figure.

Shocked beyond endurance, Dick slumped to the ground.

## Chapter 18

DICK WAS AWARE of being dry and comfortable. He lay still. Strange thoughts stirred lazily in his mind. It didn't matter if he didn't go to Wheal Mary today. They'd not yet fixed the beam. The pumps weren't working. Perhaps tomorrow he'd start work; perhaps tomorrow. Lizzy was laughing. He'd never seen Lizzy laugh before. She was a pretty girl. Jago had been freed, that's why Lizzy was laughing. He knew Jago would be freed, especially now they had their gold. What more could they want? They had Maddy too. Poor Maddy, and the mule... and the gold ... from the grave ... his father's grave ... the lantern...

"Father!" He shouted the word at the top of his voice as the vision of his father, there in the graveyard, came vividly into his mind.

His eyes were now wide open. He was sitting up. He looked wildly round the room.

The door burst open and Mrs Trewan came running in, with Lizzy just behind her.

"There, there, Dick. Everythin's fine. You're quite safe."

Dick fell back on the pillow.

Mrs Trewan gently touched his forehead. "You've had the shock of a lifetime, my poor boy," she said softly, "but it's all over now and you're safe in our cottage."

"But... but Father!" said Dick. "I saw my father!"

"You did see him. He's alive and well."

Dick barely heard her. His eyes looked past her. There, framed in the doorway, stood his father.

"Father!"

His father moved to the bed and bent over his son.

The next second they were clasping each other tightly and Dick was sobbing uncontrollably.

"Now, now, boy. Everything's going to be all right. I shouldn't 'a' done it to you, I know — I shouldn't 'a' done it."

Mrs Trewan beckoned to Lizzy, and they quietly left the room.

Gradually the boy calmed down. His father sat on the edge of the bed. His strong hands clasped his son's hand.

"I don't know what made me do it, Dick, but I thought at the time it was right. As it turned out, I've put you and your mother through hell. It'll be on my conscience for the rest of my days."

"But Father, you were lying on me. You were dead!"

"I was unconscious. I wasn't dead," said his father.

"They said you were dead."

"They thought I was dead. Even Maddy thought I was dead, until he got me laid out at his place. It was then he realised I was only unconscious. Everyone thought he was just going to measure me for my coffin, but instead he brought me round. It wasn't long before he started asking me where you and I had hidden the stuff from the *Anneke* and... well... then I had this idea."

"But why... why, Father?"

"I knew that we'd got ourselves enough money to keep us happy for the rest of our lives. A fortune. The chance of a lifetime. But the gold clearly belonged to someone who was very powerful, and who probably had a lot of influence in high places. The only way to change our lives, the way I dreamed, was to keep the gold hidden away. Then, when all the hunting and searching was over..."

Mrs Trewan came into the room. "There's food on the table. I'm sure you could do with a bite to eat."

The sight of Mrs Trewan brought back memories of Ben.

"Where's Ben?" asked Dick.

"Ben's right enough," said Mrs Trewan. "He gave the soldiers the slip. He's with your mother, breaking the news that your father's alive and well. We thought it best to break her in gently to the idea."

Dick was hungry but found it hard to eat the meal that Mrs Trewan had prepared. Everything was unreal.

Dick asked question after question. His voice seemed to echo in a dream world.

"But how did you think you'd get away with it, Father?"

"Maddy and me decided it was worth a try. The gold would be safe in my coffin, and while everyone thought I was six feet under, I'd be free to find someone willing enough to handle it for us. Someone who was used to that sort o' thing."

"Did you find someone?"

"No, and there's the pity of it. I went as far as Plymouth, but the only contacts I made were bigger rogues than me. By the time I'd 'a' paid their price there'd 'a' bin precious little left for us.

"I'd served the Devil, Dick, and 'twas 'e that now was payin' me for my sinnin' ways."

Dick remembered words like those spoken by the preacher at his father's funeral.

His father spoke on.

"I came back to tell Ben everything and ask him what he thought best to do. And what do I find? I'm in the middle of talkin' to 'im when in rushes Lizzy, tellin' us that Maddy's diggin' up the grave. Only one reason 'e was doin' that. He was tryin' to cheat me..." Tom paused. His face tightened. "But 'e'll not get away with it. I'll make sure o' that."

"He didn't, Father," said Dick, quietly.

Tom looked at his son. "What do you mean, Dick?"

"He was taking the gold to Lower Gun and walked straight into the soldiers."

Tom stared hard at his son. The startling news cut into his mind.

"They caught 'im, Father."

"The fool," said Tom, softly. He slumped in a chair and buried his face in his hands. "Then it's all bin for nothin'. The fool!"

"It's you who's the fool, Tom Tregarrick." It was Mrs Trewan who spoke. "If you'd taken Ben and Jago into your confidence earlier, none of this need have happened. What you've done is shameful and unforgiveable."

Dick looked at his father. Tom didn't speak, and Mrs Trewan, knowing she'd hit the truth of the matter, carried on.

"And would you have told Ben if your little plan had worked and you'd found someone to handle the stuff?" She paused, and in a quieter voice said, "I thought you were above the sort of greed that turns a man against his friends and puts his family through hell. 'Tis time you paid more heed to the preacher an' gave up your stealin' ways."

"Well," Tom spoke thoughtfully, "it looks as if my folly's done for me, doesn't it? Maddy will hang, and that's a fact. And who can say what a man will tell when he faces the hangman's rope?"

"You mean he's likely to tell them that you and Ben and Dick were there that night?" said Mrs Trewan. "That's what you mean don't you?"

So it wasn't all over yet.

Dick looked at his father. "Maddy was shot, Father."

All eyes turned to him. "How badly?"

"I don't know. Maddy escaped and one of the soldiers fired. I heard him cry out."

Mrs Trewan sat down, slowly. She spoke softly.

"Your greed's going to get all of you hung, including my Ben. God knows what's to become of us!"

"What'll they do to my father?" It was Lizzy's voice, gentle and tearful. She had listened to every word, and now she feared the worst. While the soldiers were looking for the gold Jago was of use to them. What now? They had their gold and two men to pay the penalty.

Jago would hang with Maddy.

## Chapter 19

TOM TREGARRICK'S homecoming was not the one he'd intended. He was no richer for his feigned death, save for a few kegs of brandy and bags of saffron. He'd moved those from the Old Men's Workings for fear that his son might try to move them and be caught in the act.

Ruth, who only two days before had witnessed her husband's burial, was in a state of shock. It remained to be seen how Chegwidden and the other folk, who'd mourned his departure, would now accept his resurrection.

Although life should have held new hope for the reunited Tregarrick family, it didn't. Ruth was finding it difficult to forgive her husband for the agonies she and her children had suffered. And they lived in fear of the soldiers. Maddy would surely tell the militia of his accomplices, particularly if they offered to spare him a stretched neck in return for information.

Could things ever be the same as they had been before the *Anneke*?

It was early afternoon and the sun shone from a deep blue, cloudless sky. Dick gazed unseeingly out of the window, listening to his father trying to work out what to do for the best.

Meg had taken Beckie and the baby to Martha Kerrow for a few hours.

"I'm not running," said Tom. "*If* the soldiers come, I'll face them. After all, it's my word against Maddy's."

"And what about Dick? It's about time you considered him," said Ruth. "You must both hide up, until it all blows over. It's foolish to wait. Go, now, while you have the chance."

Tom tried to speak calmly and reassuringly. "If we run, we're admitting our guilt. There'd never be an end to our running. If we stay, we've a chance of reasoning our way out of trouble."

The three of them talked on into the afternoon. They talked about what to tell the soldiers, and what to tell Chegwidden. Tom had to return to Wheal Mary to work. Ben had already agreed to work the Goldsworthy as a threesome.

They talked about Jago Lugg.

"It's not that I've any time for the old devil," said Tom, "especially after what he did to Dick. But it was my fault he acted the way he did. And poor Lizzy! God knows there's plenty of crimes he should swing for, but the *Anneke* isn't one of them."

"What can you do to help Jago, without getting yourself all tied up with the soldiers?" said Ruth. She had little compassion for her husband at the moment, but none at all for Lugg. Safety of her menfolk, especially Dick, mattered more to her.

"Perhaps I can get Doctor Keverne to tell them Jago was still a-bed on the night of the *Anneke*. He was sick."

There was a fierce battering on the door. They froze. Then the door shook under another fierce barrage of blows.

Tom was the first to take control of himself. "Open it, Ruth," he said quietly.

Ruth moved towards the door. Before she got there, another impatient battering blasted their ears. Trembling, she opened the door.

There in the doorway stood Jago Lugg. His eye stared out glassily from his skull, for no longer could it be called a face. The tightly drawn, white skin gave no hint of flesh beneath. It was an apparition of a man, a vision of death.

Ruth's hands gripped her apron tightly.

For the moment, Jago saw no one but the terrified

woman before him. He spoke quietly but the threat in his voice was real. "I've come for the boy."

Tom had been steeling himself to face the soldiers. Relief swept through him when he saw it was only Jago. He stepped forward and faced the man. "So . . . you've come for the boy, have you?" he asked. He rested his left hand on the lintel and leant forward looking into Jago's face.

Jago's jaw dropped. A strange sound gurgled deep in his throat, but the words would not come, try as he might to speak. His eye was opened so wide it seemed it must burst out of its socket at any moment. At last he said: "T . . . T . . . Tom Tregarrick . . . but . . . you're dead!"

"I'm more alive than you, by the looks of you."

"You . . . you're . . . " Jago stumbled over the threshold. Tom caught him as he fell and dragged him to a chair.

Life in Truro gaol had clearly been rough. Judging by the scars on his wrists, he'd been manacled, and Tom guessed by the state he was in that he'd been flogged almost to death.

"Get some brandy, Ruth."

Ruth fetched the brandy and Tom held Jago's head while they forced the liquid between his lips. He looked as near to death as it was possible to be.

Suddenly, he opened his eye and looked in turn at each of the three faces which peered down at him. His eye finally rested on Tom. "So . . . you're not dead after all!"

"No Jago — and neither are you, though you look mighty close to it." Tom spoke slowly. "Why did you come here, Jago?"

Jago turned his head to look at Dick. "I wanted your son to see what 'e'd done to me," said Jago bitterly. "I wanted 'im to know what should be on 'is conscience for the rest of 'is life."

Dick glanced from Jago to his father.

Tom bent down to speak in Jago's ear. "You're a fine one to talk about conscience. By rights I should whip the hide off you for what you did to my boy, but it looks as if someone's already done it for me."

"Your son . . ." began Jago.

"My son — nothing," snapped Tom. "It's your own stupidity. If the soldiers hadn't found the captain's papers on you, you'd never have been arrested. Silly old fool!"

"None of this would 'ave 'appened, Tom Tregarrick, if you 'adn't cut me out, just when I needed a 'elpin' 'and."

Jago's words cut deeply. They were true, and Tom knew it.

"It didn't give you the right to do what you did to Dick," said Tom.

"You're a fine one to talk of rights," said Jago quietly.

Ruth offered Jago some more brandy, which he took gratefully, indicating his thanks with a nod of his head.

"I could do with a brandy myself — as well as that skeleton," said Tom.

Ruth poured her husband a brandy.

"I must get home to my Lizzy," said Jago, but he made no move.

"Why did they let you go?" said Dick.

Jago took a long sip at his brandy. "Maddy," he said at last.

"Maddy? Where did you see Maddy?" asked Tom.

"In Truro Gaol," said Jago. "They took me to 'im. ''Ere's one o' your pals,' they said, 'one o' them what 'elped you plunder the *Anneke*'."

"And?" said Tom.

Jago looked straight at Tom, a strange faraway look in his eye. When he spoke again there was a curious softness in his voice. "Maddy told 'em 'e didn't know me from Adam. 'E said 'e'd never seen me before — and that I'd

108

never put a 'and near the gold from the *Anneke.*" Jago paused. "Maddy saved my life. That's what 'e did, 'e saved my life!"

Jago took another sip.

"What else did Maddy tell the soldiers?" said Tom.

"That's the nearest I ever seen you to bein' afraid, Tom Tregarrick," said Jago. He knew Tom was anxious to know whether Maddy had given his name to the militia or not.

"They left me alone with Maddy for the best part of an hour, while they decided what to do with me," he went on. "Maddy told me it was 'im what 'ad killed the captain, so justice 'ad been done. He said it was fate that'd stepped in. He was movin' the gold when he walked into an ambush."

"He was moving it all right," said Tom bitterly. "Thanks to him, none of us are going to be any the richer."

"Yer mean you're not going to be any the richer," snarled Jago. "Yer don't deserve a friend like Maddy, do yer know that? Yer don't deserve any friends at all."

Jago took a swig of brandy. The liquor burned life into his throat and stomach. The tension on his face eased.

"All right," said Tom, "don't tell us whether Maddy gave them our names. The tellin' of it won't change whether he did or not."

"No," said Jago, "but it would ease your mind, wouldn't it?"

Tom moved over to the door and opened it. "Goodbye, Jago."

"Maddy said 'e was the one what was caught so 'e was the one what'd pay the price."

"Noble words," said Tom. "But as the poor devil gets nearer the hangman's rope, there's no knowing what he might say."

Jago rose unsteadily to his feet. "An' who could blame 'im? Who could blame 'im, eh? Mr 'Igh an' Mighty Tom

109

Tregarrick! Well, I'll tell you this — Maddy saved my life and Maddy won't give no names."

"I hope you're right." It was Ruth who spoke, unable to contain her anxiety any longer.

Jago tottered towards the door and stopped. "I know I'm right," he said. "I know I'm right."

Jago looked at her. He decided that, for her sake, he'd speak up. "Maddy was badly shot up when they took me to 'im. 'E died before the soldiers came back to release me."

He stepped outside the door and turned to face them once more. "And 'e really died, Tom Tregarrick — in blood an' sweat an' agony. 'E saved you from swingin' and that's a fact. Yer'll never 'ave enough gold to pay the likes o' Maddy for saving your neck — and your son's."

## Chapter 20

THE WIND BATTERED them and tore at their clothes as Dick walked beside his father on their way to Wheal Mary.

The day had come to confront Chegwidden and everyone else with the proof that what Ben had been telling them for three days now was true; Tom Tregarrick was alive.

For most of the way they walked in silence.

Dick could not understand his feelings, but in some strange way he resented his father's return and the pain he'd caused his mother and the whole family. He had adjusted himself to the role of 'man' in the Tregarrick household. He had seen and felt for himself the result of his father's ill judged action.

Tom sensed his son's resentment and was saddened by the rift between them. He searched for the words which might bring them together again but, for the moment, none came. They walked in silence.

Tom looked up to the grey clouds. He felt the first splashes of rain on his face. "Best hurry or we'll be drenched," he said.

Dick quickened his pace to keep up with his father. He kept his head down. The storm clouds, which he'd seen earlier far out to sea, were almost upon them.

Before the *Anneke*, Dick's world had been a well ordered one. Everything had revolved around his father. Tom had provided the necessities of life for all of them, with his native wit, skill and natural strength. To Dick, his father had always been right.

"I'll say one thing, Dick. You've one more lesson to learn yet." It was raining much harder and Tom was having to shout above the noise of the wind.

"It's one thing for the preacher to set down plainly the Lord's rules for livin' but 'tis ordinary folk like us that 'ave to keep 'em. And 'tis a sore task, Dick."

Dick was barely listening. What did his father know of rules? He'd just put his family through days and nights of anguish and, indirectly, caused the death of one of his lifelong companions.

"You accept those rules you can," said Tom. "For the rest, you're forever reminded of 'em by Wesley's preachers with their pretty talk. But real livin' seems a deal removed at times from the way they talk. And man has ever had the power to make his own rules when the goin's hard."

"And make the goin' even harder!" Dick hurled the words at his father and quickened his step. He no longer wanted to listen.

"The man's not born that never took a wrong turnin'," shouted Tom. "That includes me. And it'll include you, Dick. Just you remember when you sits in judgement o' others."

Dick was several yards in front of his father.

He could see the engine house at Wheal Mary standing out clearly a mile away. Behind them, way out to sea, black storm clouds billowed angrily.

A white shaft of watery sunlight burst through a hole in the clouds, spotlighting the mine. The newly installed beam which crowned the engine house bobbed reassuringly, the outward sign that men toiled once more to extract the tin and copper.

Dick stopped. His father drew level with him.

"Something's up — look." Dick pointed towards the mine.

Instead of a flow of workers wending their way towards the mine, there was a stream of folk running away from it.

"Come on Dick."

Tom broke into a run and Dick ran to keep up with him.

The rain was driving hard into their faces.

"What's up, Father?" he panted. "What are they running from?"

"It's not what they're runnin' from. It's where they're runnin' to!"

A little further on they were met by Ben, coming to meet them. "Come on, come on!" he yelled. "I've been waiting this last quarter of an hour for yer!"

"Where is it?" shouted Tom.

"Greeb Point!" yelled Ben. "Norwegian schooner, hard aground! Come on!"

"No! Wait!" shouted Tom. He grabbed Ben and Dick, and stopped.

"What do you mean — wait?" yelled Ben angrily. "I've waited long enough!"

Tom ignored him. He looked at his son.

"You've a choice of work today, Dick," said Tom. "We set to work on the Goldsworthy, or we head for Greeb Point and the Norwegian schooner. What's it to be?"

Ben listened in amazement.

Dick was completely taken by surprise. "I don't know!"

"It's up to you," said his father.

"What's the matter with you Tom? Come on!" urged Ben.

"No, wait. It's Dick's decision."

Both men were looking at him. The seconds ticked by. Dick's thoughts flashed back to the night of the *Anneke*, a battling frenzy of excitement with undreamt of reward; but then the horror of the lightning at the mine and his nightmare confrontation with Lugg — a stroke of divine retribution, the preacher might say!

Ben's impatient voice cut into his thoughts.

"Come on Tom," he urged. "It could be another *Anneke*!"

"Do you think the boy's not aware o' that?" said Tom, softly.

Dick was haunted by Lizzy's sad face at the churchyard. He remembered his need to speak with her after his frantic rush from the blackness of the Old Men's Workings.

"E'll never make 'is fortune in the Goldsworthy at eight bob a pound," said Ben. "Leave 'im be. We'll miss the best pickings if we don't hurry."

Dick felt again the relief that had surged through him when Lizzy rescued him from Ben's cave, and the strength he'd gained from deciding to help her. Lizzy would know what he should decide now.

"The Goldsworthy!" The words came suddenly, and as if to stop himself having to justify his decision, he began to walk purposefully towards the mine. He wished he felt as confident as his voice had sounded.

"Dick! Dick! Wait, boy!"

Dick stopped, uncertain of what was to happen next. His father spoke urgently to Ben who gave a grunt of disgust, turned, and started off across the moor to join the wreckers.

Tom strode up to his son. "If I remember right," he said, placing an arm round the boy's shoulders, "the Goldsworthy needs two men to work it."

Dick grinned.

It was all the reassurance he needed.